Tables, Data and Formulae
for
ENGINEERS
and Mathematicians

compiled by

A. Greer, C.Eng., M.R.Ae.S.

Formerly Senior Lecturer,
Gloucestershire College of Arts and Technology
and

D. J. Hancox, B.Sc., F.I.M.A.

Head of Department of Mathematics and Computer Science
Coventry Technical College

Stanley Thornes (Publishers) Ltd

The authors and publishers gratefully acknowledge permission to reproduce copyright material in the form of the table of natural logarithms and normal distribution, as originally compiled by Messrs J White, A Yeats and G Skipworth for TABLES FOR STATISTICIANS published also by Stanley Thornes (Publishers) Ltd.

First published in 1989 by:
Stanley Thornes (Publishers) Ltd
Old Station Drive, Leckhampton
CHELTENHAM GL53 0DN England

British Library Cataloguing in Publication Data

Tables, data and formulae for engineers and
mathematicians
1. Engineering. Technical data
I. Greer, A. (Alex)
II. Hancox, D. J. (David John)
620′.00212

ISBN 0-7487-0077-3

British Standard Specification numbers referred to are those ruling at the time of publication.

References to British Standards are reproduced by kind permission of the British Standards Institution from whom can be obtained the full standard.

Typeset by Tech-Set, Gateshead, Tyne & Wear
Printed and bound in Great Britain at The Bath Press, Avon

CONTENTS

MENSURATION

Measures of length

$$1 \text{ metre (m)} = 10 \text{ decimetres (dm)}$$
$$= 100 \text{ centimetres (cm)}$$
$$= 1000 \text{ millimetres (mm)}$$
$$1 \text{ kilometre} = 1000 \text{ metres (m)}$$

$$12 \text{ inches (in)} = 1 \text{ foot (ft)}$$
$$3 \text{ feet (ft)} = 1 \text{ yard (yd)}$$
$$1760 \text{ yards (yd)} = 5280 \text{ feet (ft)} = 1 \text{ mile}$$

Approximate conversion factors are:
$$1 \text{ inch (in)} = 2.54 \text{ centimetres (cm)}$$
$$1 \text{ foot (ft)} = 30.48 \text{ centimetres (cm)}$$
$$1 \text{ yard (yd)} = 0.91 \text{ metre (m)}$$
$$1 \text{ mile} = 1.61 \text{ kilometres (km)}$$

Measures of mass or weight

$$1 \text{ gram} = 1000 \text{ milligrams (mg)}$$
$$1 \text{ kilogram} = 1000 \text{ grams (g)}$$
$$1 \text{ tonne (t)} = 1000 \text{ kilograms (kg)}$$

$$16 \text{ ounces (oz)} = 1 \text{ pound (lb)}$$
$$14 \text{ pounds (lb)} = 1 \text{ stone (st)}$$
$$112 \text{ pounds (lb)} = 1 \text{ hundredweight (cwt)}$$
$$20 \text{ hundredweights (cwt)} = 2240 \text{ pounds (lb)} = 1 \text{ ton}$$

Approximate conversion factors are:
$$1 \text{ kilogram (kg)} = 2.205 \text{ pounds (lb)}$$
$$1 \text{ pound (lb)} = 454 \text{ grams (g)}$$

Measures of capacity

$$1 \text{ litre (l)} = 100 \text{ centilitres (cl)} = 1000 \text{ cubic centimetres (cm}^3)$$
$$= 1000 \text{ millilitres (ml)}$$

$$20 \text{ fluid ounces (fl oz)} = 1 \text{ pint (pt)}$$
$$8 \text{ pints (pt)} = 1 \text{ gallon (gal)}$$

Approximate conversion factors are:
$$1 \text{ fluid ounce (fl oz)} = 28.41 \text{ millilitres (ml)}$$
$$1 \text{ litre (l)} = 1.760 \text{ pints (pt)}$$
$$1 \text{ gallon (gal)} = 4.546 \text{ litres (l)}$$

Mathematical signs and abbreviations

Symbol	Term	Symbol	Term
[{( )}]	brackets	$\lim y$	limit of y
$+$	plus	$\to a$	approaches a
$-$	minus	∞	infinity
$\pm$	plus or minus	Σ	sum of
$\lvert a-b \rvert$	modulus of difference between a and b	Π	product of
		$\sqrt{x}, x^{1/2}$	square root of x
$\times$ or $\cdot$	multiplied by	$x^{1/3}$	cube root of x
$\div$ or $/$	divided by	e	base of natural logarithms
$=$	is equal to	$\log_a x$	logarithm to the base a
$\neq$	is not equal to	$\ln x, \log_e x$	natural logarithm of x
$\equiv$	is identical with	$\lg x, \log_{10} x$	common logarithm of x
$\hat{=}$	corresponds to	antilog	antilogarithm
$\approx$	is approximately equal to	$\exp x, e^x$	exponential function of x
$\sim$	is asymptotically equal to	$n!$	factorial n
$\propto$	varies directly as	$\binom{n}{p}, {}^n C_p$	binomial coefficient
$>$	is greater than		
$<$	is less than	Δx	large increment of x
$\geqslant$	is equal to or greater than	δx	small increment of x
$\leqslant$	is equal to or less than		
$\gg$	is much greater than	D	operator $\dfrac{d}{dx}$
$\ll$	is much less than		
i, j	complex number i = j = $\sqrt{-1}$	$\int y \, dx$	indefinite integral
$\lvert z \rvert$	modulus of z	$\int_a^b y \, dx$	integral between the limits of a and b
arg z	argument of z		
x_i	ith value of the variate x	$\oint y \, dx$	around a closed contour
$\bar{x}$	average of several values of x	σ	standard deviation of a distributed variate
ρ	correlation coefficient		
r	correlation coefficient for a sample	s	standard deviation for a sample
p	probability		
$\angle$	angle	n	number in a sample
$\subset$	one subset	$\therefore$	therefore
$\mathscr{E}$	universal set	$\triangle$	triangle
A^{-1}	inverse of the matrix A	$\cup$	union
$\parallel$	parallel to	$\cap$	intersection
$\perp$	perpendicular to	A^T	transpose of the matrix A

Multiples and submultiples of units

Multiplying factor	Prefix	Abbreviation	Multiplying factor	Prefix	Abbreviation
10^{12}	tera	T	10^{-6}	micro	μ
10^{9}	giga	G	10^{-9}	nano	n
10^{6}	mega	M	10^{-12}	pico	p
10^{3}	kilo	k	10^{-15}	femto	f
10^{-3}	milli	m	10^{-18}	atto	a

Greek letters

A α alpha	Z ζ zeta	Λ λ lambda	Π π pi	Φ ϕ phi
B β beta	H η eta	M μ mu	P ρ rho	X χ chi
Γ γ gamma	Θ θ theta	N ν nu	Σ σ sigma	Ψ ψ psi
Δ δ delta	I ι iota	Ξ ξ xi	T τ tau	Ω ω omega
E ε epsilon	K κ kappa	O o omicron	Υ υ upsilon	

Standard symbols and units for physical quantities

Quantity	Symbol	Unit	Quantity	Symbol	Unit
Acceleration, gravitational	g	$m\,s^{-2}$	Flux, magnetic	Φ	Wb
Acceleration, linear	a	$m\,s^{-2}$	Force	F	N
Admittance	Y	S	Force, resisting	R	N
Altitude above sea level	z	m	Frequency	f	Hz
Amount of substance	n	mol	Frequency, resonant	f_r	Hz
Angle, plane	$\alpha, \beta, \theta, \phi$	rad			
Angle, solid	Ω, ω	steradian	Gravitational acceleration	g	$m\,s^{-2}$
Angular acceleration	α	$rad\,s^{-2}$	Gibbs function	G	J
Angular velocity	ω	$rad\,s^{-1}$	Gibbs function, specific	g	$kJ\,kg^{-1}$
Area	A	m^2			
Area, second moment of	I	m^4	Heat capacity, specific	c	$kJ\,kg^{-1}\,K^{-1}$
			Heat flow rate	Φ	W
Bulk modulus	K	$N\,m^{-2}$, Pa	Heat flux intensity	ϕ	$kW\,m^{-2}$
Capacitance	C	F	Illumination	E	lx
Capacity	V	l	Impedance	Z	Ω
Coefficient of friction	μ	no unit	Inductance, self	L	H
Coefficient of linear			Inductance, mutual	M	H
expansion	α	K^{-1}	Internal energy	U, E	J
Conductance, electrical	G	S	Internal energy, specific	u, e	$kJ\,kg^{-1}$
Conductance, thermal	h	$W\,m^{-2}\,K^{-1}$	Inertia, moment of	I, J	$kg\,m^2$
Conductivity, electrical	σ	$S\,m^{-1}$			
Conductivity, thermal	λ	$W\,m^{-1}\,K^{-1}$	Kinematic viscosity	ν	$m^2\,s^{-1}$, St
Cubical expansion,					
coefficient of	β	$°C^{-1}$	Length	l	m
Current, electrical	I	A	Light, velocity of	c	$m\,s^{-1}$
Current density	J	$A\,mm^{-2}$	Light, wavelength of	λ	m
			Linear expansion,		
Density	ρ	$kg\,m^{-3}$	coefficient of	α	K^{-1}
Density, relative	d	no unit	Luminance	L	$cd\,m^{-2}$
Dryness fraction	x	no unit	Luminous flux	Φ	lm
Dynamic viscosity	η	$N\,s\,m^{-2}$, cP	Luminous intensity	I	cd
Efficiency	η	no unit	Magnetic field strength	H	$A\,m^{-1}$
Elasticity, modulus of	E	$N\,m^{-2}$, Pa	Magnetic flux	Φ	Wb
Electric field strength	E	$V\,m^{-1}$	Magnetic flux density	B	T
Electric flux	ψ	C	Magnetomotive force	F_m	A
Electric flux density	D	$C\,m^{-2}$	Mass, macroscopic	m	kg
Energy	W	J	Modulus, bulk	K	$N\,m^{-2}$, Pa
Energy, internal	U, E	J	Modulus of elasticity	E	$N\,m^{-2}$, Pa
Energy, specific internal	u, e	$kJ\,kg^{-1}$	Modulus of section	Z	m^3
Enthalpy	H	J	Modulus, shear	G	$N\,m^{-2}$, Pa
Enthalpy, specific	h	$kJ\,kg^{-1}$	Molar mass of gas	M	$kg\,k^{-1}\,mol$
Entropy	S	$kJ\,K^{-1}$	Molar volume	V_m	$m^3\,k^{-1}\,mol$
Expansion, coefficient			Moment of force	M	$N\,m$
of cubical	β	K^{-1}	Moment of inertia	I, J	$kg\,m^2$
Expansion, coefficient			Mutual inductance	M	H
of linear	α	K^{-1}			
			Number of turns in a		
Field strength, electric	E	$V\,m^{-1}$	winding	N	no unit
Field strength, magnetic	H	$A\,m^{-2}$			
Flux density, electric	D	$C\,m^{-2}$	Periodic time	T	s
Flux density, magnetic	B	T	Permeability, absolute	μ	$H\,m^{-1}$
Flux, electric	ψ	C			

Quantity	Symbol	Unit	Quantity	Symbol	Unit
Permeability, absolute of free space	μ_0	$H\,m^{-1}$	Specific heat capacity	c	$kJ\,kg^{-1}\,K^{-1}$
Permeability, relative	μ_r	no unit	Specific volume	v	$m^3\,kg^{-1}$
Permeance	Λ	H	Strain, direct	ε	no unit
Permittivity, absolute	ε	$F\,m^{-1}$	Stress, direct	σ	$N\,m^{-2}$
Permittivity of free space	ε_0	$F\,m^{-1}$	Shear modulus of rigidity	G	$N\,m^{-2}$
Permittivity, relative	ε_r	no unit	Surface tension	γ	$N\,m^{-1}$
Poisson's ratio	ν	no unit	Susceptance	B	S
Polar moment of area	J	m^4	Temperature value	θ	°C
Power, apparent	S	V A	Temperature coefficients of resistance	α, β, γ	K^{-1}
Power, active	P	W	Thermodynamic temperature value	T	K
Power, reactive	Q	V A	Time	t	s
Pressure	p	$N\,m^{-2}$, Pa	Torque	T	N m
Quantity of heat	Q	J	Vapour velocity	C	$m\,s^{-1}$
Quantity of electricity	Q	Ah, C	Velocity	v	$m\,s^{-1}$
Reactance	X	Ω	Velocity, angular	ω	$rad\,s^{-1}$
Reluctance	S	$H^{-1}, A\,Wb^{-1}$	Velocity of light	c	$Mm\,s^{-1}$
Relative density	d	no unit	Velocity of sound	a	$m\,s^{-1}$
Resistance, electrical	R	Ω	Voltage	V	V
Resisting force	R	N	Volume	V	m^3
Resistance, temperature coefficients of	α, β, γ	$°C^{-1}$	Volume, rate of flow	V	$m^3\,s^{-1}$
Resistivity, conductors	ρ	$\Omega\,m$	Viscosity, dynamic	η	$N\,s\,m^{-2}$
Resistivity, insulators	ρ	$\Omega\,m$	Viscosity, kinematic	ν	$m^2\,s^{-1}$
Resonant frequency	f_r	Hz	Wavelength	λ	m
Second moment of area	I	m^4	Work	W	J
Self inductance	L	H			
Shear strain	γ	no unit	Young's modulus of elasticity	E	$N\,m^{-2}$
Shear stress	τ	$N\,m^{-2}$, Pa			
Specific gas constant	R	$kJ\,kg^{-1}\,K^{-1}$			

Abbreviations for units

Unit	abb.	Unit	abb.	Unit	abb.	Unit	abb.
metre	m	steradian	sr	newton	N	mole	mol
ångström	Å	radian per		bar	bar	watt	W
square metre	m^2	second	$rad\,s^{-1}$	millibar	mb	decibel	dB
cubic metre	m^3	hertz	Hz	standard		degree kelvin	K
litre	l	revolution		atmosphere	atm	degree celsius	°C
second	s	per minute	$rev\,min^{-1}$	millimetre of		coulomb	C
minute	min	kilogram	kg	mercury	mm Hg	ampere	A
hour	h	gram	g	poise	P	volt	V
lumen	lm	tonne		stoke	S, St	ohm	Ω
candela	cd	(=1 Mg)	t	joule	J	farad	F
lux	lx	siemens	S	kilowatt hour	kW h	henry	H
day	d	atomic mass		electron volt	eV	weber	Wb
year	a	unit	u	calorie	cal	tesla	T
radian	rad	pascal	Pa				

Chemical symbols and atomic masses

Element	Symbol	Atomic number	Atomic mass	Element	Symbol	Atomic number	Atomic mass
Actinium	Ac	89	(227)	Lanthanum	La	57	138.9055
Aluminium	Al	13	26.9815	Lawrencium	Lr	103	(...)
Americium	Am	95	(243)	Lead	Pb	82	207.2
Antimony	Sb	51	121.75	Lithium	Li	3	6.941
Argon	Ar	18	39.948	Lutetium	Lu	71	174.97
Arsenic	As	33	74.9216				
Astatine	At	85	~210	Magnesium	Mg	12	24.305
				Manganese	Mn	25	54.9380
Barium	Ba	56	137.34	Mendelevium	Md	101	(256)
Berkelium	Bk	97	(249)	Mercury	Hg	80	200.59
Beryllium	Be	4	9.0122	Molybdenum	Mo	42	95.94
Bismuth	Bi	83	208.9806				
Boron	B	5	10.81	Neodymium	Nd	60	144.24
Bromine	Br	35	79.904	Neon	Ne	10	20.179
				Neptunium	Np	93	(237)
Cadmium	Cd	48	112.40	Nickel	Ni	28	58.71
Caesium	Cs	55	132.9055	Niobium	Nb	41	92.9064
Californium	Cf	98	(251)	Nitrogen	N	7	14.0067
Calcium	Ca	20	40.08	Nobelium	No	102	(254)
Carbon	C	6	12.011				
Cerium	Ce	58	140.12	Osmium	Os	76	190.2
Chlorine	Cl	17	35.453	Oxygen	O	8	15.9994
Chromium	Cr	24	51.996				
Cobalt	Co	27	58.9332	Palladium	Pd	46	106.4
Copper	Cu	29	63.546	Phosphorus	P	15	30.9738
Curium	Cm	96	(247)	Platinum	Pt	78	195.09
				Plutonium	Pu	94	(242)
Dysprosium	Dy	66	162.50	Potassium	K	19	39.102
				Praseodymium	Pr	59	140.9077
Erbium	Er	68	167.26	Protactinium	Pa	91	231.0359
Europium	Eu	63	151.96	Polonium	Po	84	(210)
				Promethium	Pm	61	(145)
Fermium	Fm	100	(253)				
Fluorine	F	9	18.9984	Radium	Ra	88	226.0254
Francium	Fr	87	(223)	Radon	Rn	86	(~222)
				Rhenium	Re	75	186.2
Gadolinium	Gd	64	157.25	Rhodium	Rh	45	102.9055
Gallium	Ga	31	69.72	Rubidium	Rb	37	85.4678
Germanium	Ge	32	72.59	Ruthenium	Ru	44	101.07
Gold	Au	79	196.9665				
				Samarium	Sm	62	150.4
Hafnium	Hf	72	178.49	Scandium	Sc	21	44.9559
Helium	He	2	4.00260	Selenium	Se	34	78.96
Holmium	Ho	67	164.9303	Silicon	Si	14	28.086
Hydrogen	H	1	1.0080	Silver	Ag	47	107.868
				Sodium	Na	11	22.9898
Indium	In	49	114.82	Strontium	Sr	38	87.62
Iodine	I	53	126.9045	Sulphur	S	16	32.06
Iridium	Ir	77	192.22				
Iron	Fe	26	55.847	Tantalum	Ta	73	180.9479
				Technetium	Tc	43	(99)
Krypton	Kr	36	83.80	Tellurium	Te	52	127.60

Values in parentheses indicate the mass numbers of the most stable isotopes.

5

Element	Symbol	Atomic number	Atomic mass	Element	Symbol	Atomic number	Atomic mass
Terbium	Tb	65	158.9254	Vanadium	V	23	50.9414
Thallium	Tl	81	204.37				
Thorium	Th	90	232.0381	Xenon	Xe	54	131.30
Thulium	Tm	69	168.9342				
Tin	Sn	50	118.69	Ytterbium	Yb	70	173.04
Titanium	Ti	22	47.9	Yttrium	Y	39	88.9059
Tungsten	W	74	183.85				
				Zinc	Zn	30	65.37
Uranium	U	92	238.029	Zirconium	Zr	40	91.22

Specific heat capacity of various substances

Substance	Specific heat capacity $(kJ\ kg^{-1}\ K^{-1})$	Substance	Specific heat capacity $(kJ\ kg^{-1}\ K^{-1})$
Aluminium	0.896	Masonry, brick	0.837
Antimony	0.214	Mercury	0.138
Benzene	1.884	Naphtha	1.298
Brass	0.394	Nickel	0.456
Brickwork	0.837	Oil, machine	1.675
Cadmium	0.239	Oil, olive	1.465
Charcoal	0.837	Phosphorus	0.791
Chalk	0.900	Platinum	0.134
Coal	1.005	Quartz	0.787
Coke	0.850	Sand	0.816
Copper	0.394	Silica	0.800
Corundum	0.829	Silver	0.234
Ethanol	2.604	Soda	0.967
Ether	2.106	Steel, mild	0.486
Fusel oil	2.361	Steel, high carbon	0.490
Glass	0.812	Stone	0.837
Gold	0.130	Sulphur	0.745
Graphite	0.842	Sulphuric acid	1.382
Ice	2.110	Tin	0.234
Iron, cast	0.544	Turpentine	1.976
Iron, wrought	0.461	Water	4.187
Kerosene	2.093	Wood, fir	2.721
Lead	0.130	Wood, oak	2.387
Limestone	0.909	Wood, pine	1.955
Magnesia	0.930	Zinc	0.398
Marble	0.879		

Boiling points at atmospheric pressure

Substance	Boiling point (°C)	Substance	Boiling point (°C)	Substance	Boiling point (°C)
Ammonia	−33.5	Linseed oil	264	Sulphuric acid	338
Benzene	80	Mercury	356.7	Trichloromethane	
Brine	108	Methanol	66	(chloroform)	62
Bromine	58.8	Naphthalene	220	Water, pure	100
Ethanol	78.4	Nitric acid	120	Water, sea	100.7
Ether	38	Turpentine	157		

Loudness of sounds (0 dB is 2.10^{-5} N m^{-2} r.m.s.)

Source	Intensity (dB)	Source	Intensity (dB)
Threshold of hearing	0	Loud conversation	70
Virtual silence	10	Door slamming	80
Quiet room	20	Riveting gun	90
Average home	30	Loud motor horn	100
Motor car	40	Thunder	110
Ordinary conversation	50	Aero-engine	120
Street traffic	60	Threshold of pain	130

Densities of various substances

Substance	Density (kg m^{-3})	Substance	Density (kg m^{-3})	Substance	Density (kg m^{-3})
Ammonia	890	Ethoxyethane	720	Petroleum oil	820
Asbestos	2800	Fluoric acid	1500	Phenol	960
Benzene	690	Gasoline	700	Phosphorus	1800
Borax	1750	Glass	2600	Phosphoric (v) acid	1780
Brick, common	1800	Granite	2650	Quartz	2600
Brick, fire	2300	Gravel	1750	Rape seed oil	920
Brick, hard	2000	Gypsum	2200	Salt, common	2100
Brick, pressed	2150	Hydrochloric acid	1200	Sand, dry	1600
Brickwork in mortar	1600	Ice	900	Sand, wet	2000
Brickwork in cement	1800	Ivory	1850	Sandstone	2300
Cement	3100	Kerosene	800	Slate	2800
Chalk	2600	Limestone	2600	Soapstone	2700
Charcoal	400	Linseed oil	920	Soil, black	2000
Coal, anthracite	1500	Marble	2700	Sulphur	2000
Coal, bituminous	1270	Masonry	2400	Sulphuric acid	1840
Concrete	2200	Mica	2800	Tar	1000
Carbon disulphide	1260	Mineral oil	920	Tile	1800
Cotton seed oil	930	Mortar	1500	Turpentine	870
Earth, loose	1200	Naphtha	760	Vinegar	1080
Earth, rammed	1600	Nitric acid	1220	Water	1000
Emery	4000	Olive oil	920	Water, sea	1030
Ethanol	790	Palm oil	970		

Densities of metals

Metal	Density (kg m^{-3})	Metal	Density (kg m^{-3})	Metal	Density (kg m^{-3})
Aluminium	2700	Lead	11370	Silver	10530
Copper	8900	Mercury	13580	Tungsten	19300
Gold	19300	Nickel	8800	Zinc	6860
Iron	7850	Platinum	21040		

Latent heat of evaporation

Liquid	(kJ kg^{-1})	Liquid	(kJ kg^{-1})	Liquid	(kJ kg^{-1})
Ammonia	1230	Ethanol	863	Sulphur dioxide	381
Carbon		Ether	379	Turpentine	309
hydrogensulphate	372	Methanol	1119	Water	2248

Latent heat of fusion

Substance	(kJ kg^{-1})	Substance	(kJ kg^{-1})	Substance	(kJ kg^{-1})
Aluminium	387	Ice	334.9	Phosphorus	21.1
Bismuth	52.9	Kerosene	147.2	Silver	88.2
Cast iron, grey	96.3	Lead	23.3	Sulphur	39.2
Cast iron, white	138.2	Magnesium	372	Tin	59.7
Copper	180	Nickel	309	Zinc	117.8

Abbreviations for words

Word	abb.	Word	abb.	Word	abb.	Word	abb.
absolute	abs.	crystalline	cryst.	freezing		recrystallised	recryst.
alternating		decompo-		point	f.p.	relative	
current	a.c.	sition	decomp.	infra-red	i.r.	humidity	r.h.
anhydrous	anhyd.	dilute	dil.	magneto-		root mean	
aqueous	aq.	direct current	d.c.	motive		square	r.m.s.
boiling point	b.p.	electromotive		force	m.m.f.	temperature	temp.
calculated	calc.	force	e.m.f.	maximum	max.	standard	
concentrated	conc.	equation	eqn.	melting point	m.p.	temp. and	
constant	const.	equivalent	equiv.	minimum	min.	pressure	s.t.p.
corrected	corr.	experi-		potential		ultra violet	u.v.
critical	crit.	ment(al)	expt.	difference	p.d.		

Commonly used constants

Constant	Numerical value	Logarithm	Constant	Numerical value	Logarithm
π	3.141 593	0.4972	$1/\pi$	0.318 310	$\overline{1}$.5029
2π	6.283 185	0.7982	$\sqrt{\pi}$	1.772 454	0.2486
$\pi/4$	0.785 398	$\overline{1}$.8951	e	2.718 28	0.4343
π^2	9.869 604	0.9943	g	9.81 m s^{-2}	0.9917

Fixed points

Boiling point of liquid oxygen	$-182.97\,°C$
Melting point of ice (secondary point)	$0.00\,°C$
Triple point of water	$0.01\,°C$
Boiling point of water	$100\,°C$
Freezing point of zinc (secondary point)	$419.505\,°C$
Boiling point of liquid sulphur	$444.60\,°C$
Freezing point of liquid antimony	$630.50\,°C$
Melting point of silver	$960.80\,°C$
Melting point of gold	$1063.00\,°C$

Atmospheric pressure = 760 mm Hg = 1013 mb   1 bar = 10^5 Pa

Diameter of the earth = 12 750 km at the equator and 12 710 km at the poles.

Average radius of the earth = 6371 km

Speed of rotation of the earth at the equator = 1670 km h^{-1}

ARITHMETIC

Sequence of arithmetic operations

When numbers are combined in a series of arithmetical operations:

(i) First work out brackets.

(ii) Multiply and/or divide.

(iii) Add and/or subtract.

Thus $12 + 4 + 7 \times (3 + 2) - 8 = 12 + 4 + 7 \times 5 - 8$
$$= 12 + 4 + 35 - 8 = 43.$$

Ratio

A ratio may be expressed as a fraction and vice versa. Thus $2:3$ is the same as $\frac{2}{3}$ and $\frac{3}{4}$ is the same as $3:4$.

Percentages

To convert a fraction or a decimal into a percentage, multiply it by 100. Thus $\frac{2}{5} = \frac{2}{5} \times 100\% = 40\%$ and $0.63 \times 100\% = 63\%$.

A percentage can be converted into a fraction or decimal by dividing it by 100. Thus $85\% = 85 \div 100 = 0.85$.

Percentage profit

$$\text{Profit \%} = \frac{\text{selling price} - \text{cost price}}{\text{cost price}} \times 100.$$

Profit % is often referred to as *mark up*.

Percentage loss

$$\text{Loss \%} = \frac{\text{cost price} - \text{selling price}}{\text{cost price}} \times 100.$$

Margin

$$\text{Margin \%} = \frac{\text{selling price} - \text{cost price}}{\text{selling price}} \times 100.$$

Gross profit

Gross profit = turnover − cost price.

Net profit

Net profit = gross profit − overheads.

9

Discount	$$\text{Cash price} = \frac{\text{marked price} \times (100 - \text{discount \%})}{100}.$$
Commission	$$\text{Amount of commission} = \text{amount of sales} \times \frac{\text{commission \%}}{100}.$$
Value added tax	$$\text{Amount of VAT} = \text{price of goods} \times \frac{\text{rate of VAT \%}}{100}.$$
Rates	Rates payable per annum = rateable value of the property $\times$ rate in the £1.
Income tax	Taxable income = gross income − allowances. $$\text{Tax payable} = \text{taxable income} \times \frac{\text{rate of tax \%}}{100}.$$

Simple interest

$$I = \frac{PRT}{100}$$

$$A = \left(1 + \frac{TR}{100}\right)P$$

P = principal (i.e., amount of money invested or borrowed)
R = percentage rate per annum
T = time in years
A = amount after T years

Compound interest

$$A = P\left(1 + \frac{R}{100}\right)^T$$

A = amount of the investment after T years
P = principal or amount invested
R = percentage rate per annum

If the interest is added n times per annum:

$$A = P\left(1 + \frac{R}{100n}\right)^{nT}$$

Depreciation

$$A = P\left(1 - \frac{R}{100}\right)^T$$

A = value after T years
P = initial cost of asset
R = rate of depreciation (% per annum)

Shares

Amount paid for the shares = number of shares bought $\times$ price paid per share.

Nominal value of shares bought = number of shares bought $\times$ nominal value per share.

Amount of dividend per share = nominal value per share $\times \dfrac{\text{declared dividend \%}}{100}.$

Stock

Interest payable on stock = nominal amount of stock bought $\times \dfrac{\text{interest \%}}{100}.$

Bankruptcy

$$\text{Declared dividend} = \frac{\text{net assets} - \text{amount owed to secured creditors}}{\text{total liabilities}}.$$

SIMPLE INTEREST

Appreciation of £1 for periods from 1 year to 24 years

Year	5%	6%	7%	8%	9%	10%	11%	12%	13%	14%
1	1.050	1.060	1.070	1.080	1.090	1.100	1.110	1.120	1.130	1.140
2	1.100	1.120	1.140	1.160	1.180	1.200	1.220	1.240	1.260	1.280
3	1.150	1.180	1.210	1.240	1.270	1.300	1.330	1.360	1.390	1.420
4	1.200	1.240	1.280	1.320	1.360	1.400	1.440	1.480	1.520	1.560
5	1.250	1.300	1.350	1.400	1.450	1.500	1.550	1.600	1.650	1.700
6	1.300	1.360	1.420	1.480	1.540	1.600	1.660	1.720	1.780	1.840
7	1.350	1.420	1.490	1.560	1.630	1.700	1.770	1.840	1.910	1.980
8	1.400	1.480	1.560	1.640	1.720	1.800	1.880	1.960	2.040	2.120
9	1.450	1.540	1.630	1.720	1.810	1.900	1.990	2.080	2.170	2.260
10	1.500	1.600	1.700	1.800	1.900	2.000	2.100	2.200	2.300	2.400
11	1.550	1.660	1.770	1.880	1.990	2.100	2.210	2.320	2.430	2.540
12	1.600	1.720	1.840	1.960	2.080	2.200	2.320	2.440	2.560	2.680
13	1.650	1.780	1.910	2.040	2.170	2.300	2.430	2.560	2.690	2.820
14	1.700	1.840	1.980	2.120	2.260	2.400	2.540	2.680	2.820	2.960
15	1.750	1.900	2.050	2.200	2.350	2.500	2.650	2.800	2.950	3.100
16	1.800	1.960	2.120	2.280	2.440	2.600	2.760	2.920	3.080	3.240
17	1.850	2.020	2.190	2.360	2.530	2.700	2.870	3.040	3.210	3.380
18	1.900	2.080	2.260	2.440	2.620	2.800	2.980	3.160	3.340	3.520
19	1.950	2.140	2.330	2.520	2.710	2.900	3.090	3.280	3.470	3.660
20	2.000	2.200	2.400	2.600	2.800	3.000	3.200	3.400	3.600	3.800
21	2.050	2.260	2.470	2.680	2.890	3.100	3.310	3.520	3.730	3.940
22	2.100	2.320	2.540	2.760	2.980	3.200	3.420	3.640	3.860	4.080
23	2.150	2.380	2.610	2.840	3.070	3.300	3.530	3.760	3.990	4.220
24	2.200	2.440	2.680	2.920	3.160	3.400	3.640	3.880	4.120	4.360

COMPOUND INTEREST

Appreciation of £1 for periods from 1 year to 24 years

Year	5%	6%	7%	8%	9%	10%	11%	12%	13%	14%
1	1.050	1.060	1.070	1.080	1.090	1.100	1.110	1.120	1.130	1.140
2	1.103	1.124	1.145	1.166	1.188	1.210	1.232	1.254	1.277	1.300
3	1.158	1.191	1.225	1.260	1.295	1.331	1.368	1.405	1.443	1.482
4	1.216	1.262	1.311	1.360	1.412	1.464	1.518	1.574	1.603	1.689
5	1.276	1.338	1.403	1.469	1.539	1.611	1.685	1.762	1.842	1.925
6	1.340	1.419	1.501	1.587	1.677	1.772	1.870	1.974	2.082	2.195
7	1.407	1.504	1.606	1.714	1.828	1.949	2.076	2.211	2.353	2.502
8	1.477	1.594	1.718	1.851	1.993	2.144	2.304	2.476	2.658	2.853
9	1.551	1.689	1.838	1.999	2.172	2.358	2.558	2.773	3.004	3.252
10	1.629	1.791	1.967	2.159	2.367	2.594	2.839	3.106	3.395	3.707
11	1.710	1.898	2.105	2.332	2.580	2.853	3.152	3.479	3.836	4.226
12	1.796	2.012	2.252	2.518	2.813	3.138	3.498	3.896	4.335	4.818
13	1.886	2.133	2.410	2.720	3.066	3.452	3.883	4.363	4.898	5.492
14	1.980	2.261	2.579	2.937	3.342	3.797	4.310	4.887	5.535	6.261
15	2.079	2.397	2.759	3.172	3.642	4.177	4.785	5.474	6.254	7.138
16	2.183	2.540	2.952	3.426	3.970	4.595	5.311	6.130	7.067	8.137
17	2.292	2.693	3.159	3.700	4.328	5.054	5.895	6.866	7.986	9.276
18	2.407	2.854	3.380	3.996	4.717	5.560	6.544	7.690	9.024	10.575
19	2.527	3.026	3.617	4.316	5.142	6.116	7.263	8.613	10.197	12.056
20	2.653	3.207	3.870	4.661	5.604	6.727	8.062	9.646	11.523	13.743
21	2.786	3.400	4.141	5.034	6.109	7.400	8.949	10.804	13.021	15.668
22	2.925	3.604	4.430	5.437	6.659	8.140	9.934	12.100	14.714	17.861
23	3.072	3.820	4.741	5.871	7.258	8.954	11.026	13.552	16.627	20.362
24	3.225	4.049	5.072	6.341	7.911	9.850	12.239	15.179	18.788	23.212

ALGEBRA

Factors

$$(a + b)^2 = a^2 + 2ab + b^2$$
$$(a - b)^2 = a^2 - 2ab + b^2$$
$$a^3 + b^3 = (a + b)(a^2 - ab + b^2)$$
$$a^3 - b^3 = (a - b)(a^2 + ab + b^2)$$
$$a^2 - b^2 = (a + b)(a - b)$$
$$(a + b)^3 = a^3 + 3a^2b + 3ab^2 + b^3$$
$$(a - b)^3 = a^3 - 3a^2b + 3ab^2 - b^3$$
$$(a + b + c + \ldots)^2 = a^2 + b^2 + c^2 + \ldots + 2a(b + c + \ldots)$$
$$+ 2b(c + \ldots) + \ldots$$

Indices

$$a^m \times a^n = a^{m+n}$$
$$a^m \div a^n = a^{m-n}$$
$$(a^m)^n = a^{mn}$$
$$\sqrt[n]{a^m} = a^{m/n}$$
$$\frac{1}{a^n} = a^{-n}$$
$$a^0 = 1$$
$$(a^n b^m)^p = a^{np} b^{mp}$$
$$\left(\frac{a}{b}\right)^n = \frac{a^n}{b^n}$$
$$\sqrt[n]{ab} = \sqrt[n]{a} \times \sqrt[n]{b}$$
$$\sqrt[n]{\frac{a}{b}} = \frac{\sqrt[n]{a}}{\sqrt[n]{b}}$$

Logarithms

If $N = a^x$ then $\log_a N = x$ and $N = a^{\log_a N}$.

$$\log_a N = \frac{\log_b N}{\log_b a}$$
$$\log(ab) = \log a + \log b$$
$$\log\left(\frac{a}{b}\right) = \log a - \log b$$
$$\log a^n = n \log a$$
$$\log \sqrt[n]{a} = \frac{1}{n} \log a$$
$$\log_a 1 = 0$$
$$\log_e N = 2.3026 \log_{10} N$$

Proportion

If $\dfrac{a}{b} = \dfrac{c}{d}$ then $\dfrac{a + b}{b} = \dfrac{c + d}{d}$

$$\frac{a - b}{b} = \frac{c - d}{d}$$
$$\frac{a - b}{a + b} = \frac{c - d}{c + d}$$

Quadratic equations	If $ax^2 + bx + c = 0$

$$x = \frac{-b \pm \sqrt{b^2 - 4ac}}{2a}$$

If $b^2 - 4ac > 0$ the equation $ax^2 + bx + c = 0$ yields two real and different roots.

If $b^2 - 4ac = 0$ the equation $ax^2 + bx + c = 0$ yields coincident roots.

If $b^2 - 4ac < 0$ the equation $ax^2 + bx + c = 0$ has complex roots.

Graphs

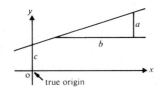

$$m = \frac{a}{b}$$

The equation of a straight line can be written in the form $y = mx + c$ where m is the gradient of the line and c is the intercept on the y-axis.

Non-linear relationships can sometimes be converted into linear relationships. The most common of these are given in the table below:

Equation	Plot	Gradient	Intercept
$y = ax^n + b$	y v. x^n	a	b
$y = \dfrac{a}{x^n} + b$	y v. $\dfrac{1}{x^n}$	a	b
$y = a\sqrt[n]{x} + b$	y v. $\sqrt[n]{x}$	a	b
$y = ax^n + bx^{n-1}$	$\dfrac{y}{x^{n-1}}$ v. x	a	b
$y = ax^n$	$\log y$ v. $\log x$	n	$\log a$
$y = ab^x$	$\log y$ v. x	$\log b$	$\log a$
$y = ae^{bx}$	$\log y$ v. x	$b \log e$	$\log a$

Variation

If $y \propto x$ then $y = kx$, where k is a constant. This is direct variation.

If $y \propto \dfrac{1}{x}$ then $y = \dfrac{k}{x}$. This is inverse variation.

If p varies directly as t and inversely as v then $p = \dfrac{kt}{v}$.

This is joint variation.

Arithmetic progression

$a, a + d, a + 2d, a + 3d, \ldots a + (n-1)d$

Sum of n terms $= n/2\,[2a + (n-1)d]$

Geometric progression

$a, ar, ar^2, ar^3, \ldots ar^{n-1}$

$$\text{Sum of } n \text{ terms} = \frac{a(r^n - 1)}{r - 1} \quad \text{or} \quad \frac{a(1 - r^n)}{1 - r}$$

$$r > 1 \qquad\qquad r < 1$$

$$\text{Sum to infinity when } r < 1 = \frac{a}{1 - r}$$

Binomial theorem

$$(a + b)^n = a^n + na^{n-1}b + \frac{n(n-1)\,a^{n-2}b^2}{2!} + \ldots b^n$$

$$(1 + x)^n = 1 + nx + \frac{n(n-1)\,x^2}{2!} + \ldots x^n$$

If n is a positive integer the series is finite and is true for all values of x. If n is negative or fractional the series is infinite and is valid only if x lies between -1 and $+1$.

Series

$$e = 1 + 1 + \frac{1}{2!} + \frac{1}{3!} + \ldots$$

$$e^x = 1 + x + \frac{x^2}{2!} + \frac{x^3}{3!} + \ldots$$

$$e^{-x} = 1 - x + \frac{x^2}{2!} - \frac{x^3}{3!} + \ldots$$

Taylor's expansion

$$f(x + a) = f(x) + af'(x) + \frac{a^2}{2!}f''(x) + \frac{a^3}{3!}f'''(x) + \ldots$$

Maclaurin's form

$$f(x) = f(0) + xf'(0) + \frac{x^2}{2!}f''(0) + \frac{x^3}{3!}f'''(0) + \ldots$$

Logarithmic

$$\log_e(1 + x) = x - \frac{x^2}{2} + \frac{x^3}{3} - \frac{x^4}{4} + \ldots \qquad (\text{for } -1 < x \leqslant 1)$$

$$\log_e(1 - x) = -x - \frac{x^2}{2} - \frac{x^3}{3} - \frac{x^4}{4} + \ldots \qquad (\text{for } -1 \leqslant x < 1)$$

$$\log_e\left(\frac{1 + x}{1 - x}\right) = 2\left[x + \frac{x^3}{3} + \frac{x^5}{5} + \ldots\right]$$

Trigonometric

$$\sin x = x - \frac{x^3}{3!} + \frac{x^5}{5!} - \frac{x^7}{7!} + \ldots \quad x \text{ in radians}$$

$$\cos x = 1 - \frac{x^2}{2!} + \frac{x^4}{4!} - \frac{x^6}{6!} + \ldots \quad x \text{ in radians}$$

$$\text{arc}\sin x = x + \frac{1}{2} \times \frac{x^3}{3} + \frac{1}{2} \times \frac{3}{4} \times \frac{x^5}{5} + \frac{1}{2} \times \frac{3}{4} \times \frac{5}{6} \times \frac{x^7}{7} + \ldots$$

Hyperbolic

$$\sinh x = x + \frac{x^3}{3!} + \frac{x^5}{5!} + \ldots$$

$$\cosh x = 1 + \frac{x^2}{2!} + \frac{x^4}{4!} + \ldots$$

MENSURATION OF PLANE FIGURES

Rectangle

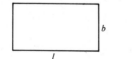

Area $= lb$

Perimeter $= 2l + 2b$

Parallelogram

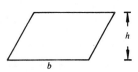

Area $= bh$

Triangle

Area $= \frac{1}{2}bh = \sqrt{s(s-a)(s-b)(s-c)}$

$\quad\quad = \frac{1}{2}ab \sin C$

Where $s = \dfrac{a+b+c}{2}$

Trapezium

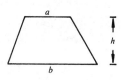

Area $= \frac{1}{2}h(a+b)$

Polygon (regular)

Area $= \frac{1}{4}nl^2 \cot \dfrac{180}{n}$

(n is the number of sides of length l)

Circle

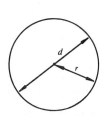

Area $= \pi r^2 = \dfrac{\pi d^2}{4}$

Circumference $= \pi d = 2\pi r$

Segment of a circle

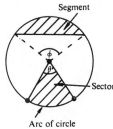
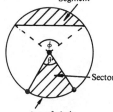

Area $= \frac{1}{2}r^2(\phi - \sin \phi)$

(ϕ in radians)

Sector of a circle

Area $= \pi r^2 \times \dfrac{\theta}{360}$

Length of arc $= 2\pi r \times \dfrac{\theta}{360}$

(θ in degrees)

Ellipse

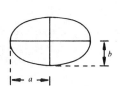

Circumference $= 2\pi\sqrt{\frac{1}{2}(a^2 + b^2)}$ approx.

Area $= \pi ab$

VOLUMES AND SURFACE AREAS

Cylinder

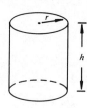

Volume $= \pi r^2 h$

Curved surface area $= 2\pi rh$

Total surface area $\quad = 2\pi rh + 2\pi r^2$

$\qquad\qquad\qquad\qquad = 2\pi r(r + h)$

Any solid having a uniform cross-section

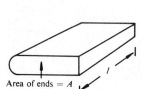

Area of ends $= A$

Volume $= Al$

Curved surface area

$\qquad =$ perimeter of cross-section $\times$ length

Total surface area

$\qquad =$ curved surface area $+$ area of ends

Cone

Volume $= \frac{1}{3}\pi r^2 h \qquad$ ($h =$ vertical height)

Curved surface area $= \pi rl \quad$ ($l =$ slant height)

Total surface area $= \pi rl + \pi r^2$

Sphere

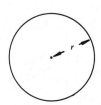

Volume $= \frac{4}{3}\pi r^3$

Surface area $= 4\pi r^2$

Frustrum of a cone

Volume $= \frac{1}{3}\pi h\,(R^2 + Rr + r^2)$

Curved surface area $= \pi(R + r)l$

Total surface area $= \pi(R + r)l + \pi R^2 + \pi r^2$

Pyramid

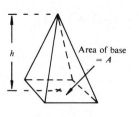

Area of base $= A$

Volume $= \frac{1}{3}Ah$

Prism

Any solid with two faces parallel and having a constant cross-section. The end faces must be triangles, quadrilaterals or polygons.

Volume $=$ area of cross-section $\times$ length of prism

ANGLES

1 revolution $360° = 2\pi$ radians

$$60' = 1°$$

$$60'' = 1'$$

$$1° = \frac{2\pi}{360} \text{ radians}$$

$$1 \text{ radian} = \frac{360}{2\pi} = 57.3°$$

$$45° = \frac{\pi}{4} \text{ radians} \qquad 90° = \frac{\pi}{2} \text{ radians}$$

$$60° = \frac{\pi}{3} \text{ radians} \qquad 180° = \pi \text{ radians}$$

$$120° = \frac{2\pi}{3} \text{ radians} \qquad 270° = \frac{3\pi}{2} \text{ radians}$$

Acute angle
(less than 90°)

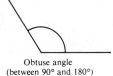

Obtuse angle
(between 90° and 180°)

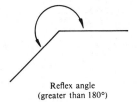

Reflex angle
(greater than 180°)

Complementary angles are angles whose sum is 90°.

Supplementary angles are angles whose sum is 180°.

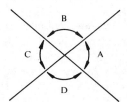

The vertically opposite angles are equal

$\angle A = \angle C$ and $\angle B = \angle D$

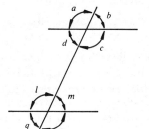

When two parallel lines are cut by a transversal

(i)   The corresponding angles are equal:
      $a = l; b = m; c = p; d = q$
(ii) The alternate angles are equal:
      $d = m; c = l$
(iii) The interior angles are supplementary:
      $d + l = 180°; c + m = 180°$

17

TRIANGLES

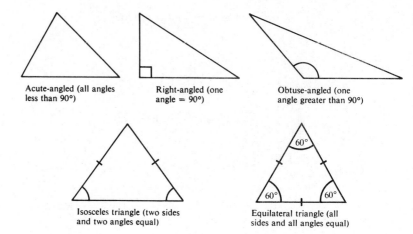

Acute-angled (all angles less than 90°)

Right-angled (one angle = 90°)

Obtuse-angled (one angle greater than 90°)

Isosceles triangle (two sides and two angles equal)

Equilateral triangle (all sides and all angles equal)

The sum of the angles of a triangle equals 180°

Pythagoras' theorem

In a right-angled triangle the square on the hypotenuse is equal to the sum of the squares on the other two sides.

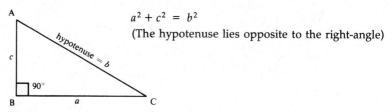

$$a^2 + c^2 = b^2$$

(The hypotenuse lies opposite to the right-angle)

Congruency

Two triangles are congruent if they are equal in every respect. Any of the following are sufficient to prove that two triangles are congruent:

(i)   One side and two angles in one triangle equal to one side and two similarly located angles in the second triangle.

(ii) Two sides and the angle between them in one triangle equal to two sides and the angle between them in the second triangle.

(iii) Three sides of one triangle equal to three sides in the second triangle.

(iv) In right-angled triangles the hypotenuses are equal and one other side in each triangle also equal.

Similar triangles

Two triangles are similar if they are equi-angular. If in △s ABC and XYZ, $\angle A = \angle X$, $\angle B = \angle Y$, and $\angle C = \angle Z$ then

$$\frac{AB}{XY} = \frac{AC}{XZ} = \frac{BC}{YZ}$$

Any of the following is sufficient to prove that two triangles are similar:

(i)   Two angles in one triangle equal to two angles in the second triangle.

(ii) Two sides in one triangle are proportional to two sides in the second triangle and the angle between these sides in each triangle is equal.

(iii) Three sides in one triangle are proportional to the three sides in the second triangle.

GEOMETRY OF THE CIRCLE

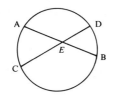

AE × EB = CE × ED

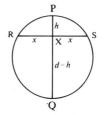

PQ = diameter (d)
RS ⊥ PQ
PX = h
RX = XS = x

$h(d - h) = x^2$

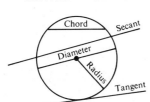

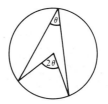

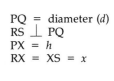

The angle which an arc of a circle subtends at the centre of a circle is twice the angle which the arc subtends at the circumference.

The tangent to a circle is at right-angles to a radius drawn from the point of tangency.

Lengths of chords for spacing off a given number of divisions or holes on the circumference of a circle with unit diameter

Holes or divisions	Length of chord	Holes or divisions	Length of chord	Holes or divisions	Length of chord
3	0.866 025	19	0.164 594	35	0.089 639
4	0.707 106			36	0.087 155
		20	0.156 434	37	0.084 805
5	0.587 785	21	0.149 042	38	0.082 579
6	0.500 000	22	0.142 314	39	0.080 466
7	0.433 883	23	0.136 166		
8	0.382 683	24	0.130 526	40	0.078 459
9	0.342 020			41	0.076 549
		25	0.125 333	42	0.074 730
10	0.309 017	26	0.120 536	43	0.072 995
11	0.281 732	27	0.116 092	44	0.071 339
12	0.258 819	28	0.111 964		
13	0.239 315	29	0.108 119	45	0.069 756
14	0.222 520			46	0.068 242
		30	0.104 528	47	0.066 792
15	0.207 911	31	0.101 168	48	0.065 403
16	0.195 090	32	0.098 017	49	0.064 070
17	0.183 749	33	0.095 056	50	0.062 790
18	0.173 648	34	0.092 268		

The above values are for circles with unit diameter. For circles of other diameters the figures given must be multiplied by the diameter.

19

Example For 9 holes on a circle of diameter 15 cm the chord length is 15 × 0.342 020 = 5.1303 cm.

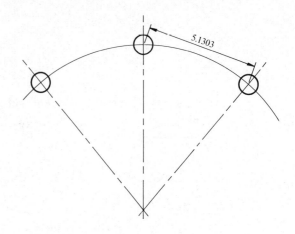

TRIGONOMETRY

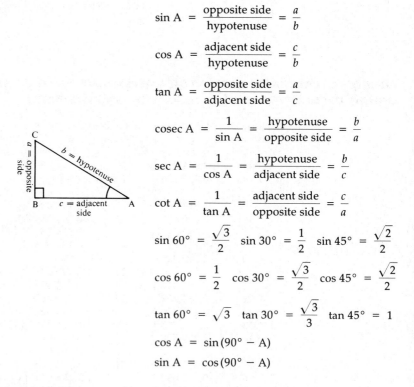

$$\sin A = \frac{\text{opposite side}}{\text{hypotenuse}} = \frac{a}{b}$$

$$\cos A = \frac{\text{adjacent side}}{\text{hypotenuse}} = \frac{c}{b}$$

$$\tan A = \frac{\text{opposite side}}{\text{adjacent side}} = \frac{a}{c}$$

$$\operatorname{cosec} A = \frac{1}{\sin A} = \frac{\text{hypotenuse}}{\text{opposite side}} = \frac{b}{a}$$

$$\sec A = \frac{1}{\cos A} = \frac{\text{hypotenuse}}{\text{adjacent side}} = \frac{b}{c}$$

$$\cot A = \frac{1}{\tan A} = \frac{\text{adjacent side}}{\text{opposite side}} = \frac{c}{a}$$

$$\sin 60° = \frac{\sqrt{3}}{2} \quad \sin 30° = \frac{1}{2} \quad \sin 45° = \frac{\sqrt{2}}{2}$$

$$\cos 60° = \frac{1}{2} \quad \cos 30° = \frac{\sqrt{3}}{2} \quad \cos 45° = \frac{\sqrt{2}}{2}$$

$$\tan 60° = \sqrt{3} \quad \tan 30° = \frac{\sqrt{3}}{3} \quad \tan 45° = 1$$

$$\cos A = \sin(90° - A)$$

$$\sin A = \cos(90° - A)$$

Trigonometrical identities

$$\sin^2 A + \cos^2 A = 1 \qquad \sec^2 A = 1 + \tan^2 A$$

$$\operatorname{cosec}^2 A = 1 + \cot^2 A \qquad \tan A = \frac{\sin A}{\cos A}$$

The general angle

Quadrant	Angle	sin A =	cos A =	tan A =
first	0° to 90°	sin A	cos A	tan A
second	90° to 180°	$\sin(180° - A)$	$-\cos(180° - A)$	$-\tan(180° - A)$
third	180° to 270°	$-\sin(A - 180°)$	$-\cos(A - 180°)$	$\tan(A - 180°)$
fourth	270° to 360°	$-\sin(360° - A)$	$\cos(360° - A)$	$-\tan(360° - A)$

For any triangle

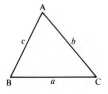

Sine rule

$$\frac{a}{\sin A} = \frac{b}{\sin B} = \frac{c}{\sin C}$$

Cosine rule

$$a^2 = b^2 + c^2 - 2bc \cos A$$
$$b^2 = a^2 + c^2 - 2ac \cos B$$
$$c^2 = a^2 + b^2 - 2ab \cos C$$

Tangent rule

$$\tan\frac{B - C}{2} = \frac{b - c}{b + c} \cot\frac{A}{2}$$

Half-angle formulae

$$\sin\frac{A}{2} = \sqrt{\frac{(s - b)(s - c)}{bc}}$$

$$\cos\frac{A}{2} = \sqrt{\frac{s(s - a)}{bc}}$$

$$\tan\frac{A}{2} = \sqrt{\frac{(s - b)(s - c)}{s(s - a)}}$$

where $s = \frac{1}{2}(a + b + c)$

Double-angle formulae

$$\sin 2A = 2 \sin A \cos A$$
$$\cos 2A = \cos^2 A - \sin^2 A$$
$$= 2 \cos^2 A - 1$$
$$= 1 - 2 \sin^2 A$$

$$\sin^2 A = \frac{1 - \cos 2A}{2}$$

$$\cos^2 A = \frac{1 + \cos 2A}{2}$$

$$\tan 2A = \frac{2 \tan A}{1 - \tan^2 A}$$

$$\left. \begin{array}{l} \sin A = \dfrac{2t}{1 + t^2} \\[2mm] \cos A = \dfrac{1 - t^2}{1 + t^2} \end{array} \right\} \quad \text{where } t = \tan\frac{A}{2}$$

Factor formulae

$$\cos P + \cos Q = 2 \cos \frac{P+Q}{2} \cos \frac{P-Q}{2}$$

$$\cos P - \cos Q = -2 \sin \frac{P+Q}{2} \sin \frac{P-Q}{2}$$

$$\sin P + \sin Q = 2 \sin \frac{P+Q}{2} \cos \frac{P-Q}{2}$$

$$\sin P - \sin Q = 2 \cos \frac{P+Q}{2} \sin \frac{P-Q}{2}$$

Multiple angles

$$\sin (A \pm B) = \sin A \cos B \pm \cos A \sin B$$

$$\cos (A \pm B) = \cos A \cos B \mp \sin A \sin B$$

$$\tan (A \pm B) = \frac{\tan A \pm \tan B}{1 \mp \tan A \tan B}$$

$$2 \sin A \cos B = \sin (A + B) + \sin (A - B)$$

$$2 \sin A \sin B = \cos (A - B) - \cos (A + B)$$

$$2 \cos A \cos B = \cos (A + B) + \cos (A - B)$$

$$R \sin (\omega t \pm \alpha) = a \sin \omega t \pm b \cos \omega t$$

$$\text{where } R = \sqrt{a^2 + b^2} \text{ and } \tan \alpha = \frac{b}{a}$$

HYPERBOLIC FUNCTIONS

$$\sinh x = \tfrac{1}{2}(e^x - e^{-x})$$

$$\cosh x = \tfrac{1}{2}(e^x + e^{-x})$$

$$\tanh x = \frac{\sinh x}{\cosh x} = \frac{e^{2x} - 1}{e^{2x} + 1}$$

$$\operatorname{cosech} x = \frac{1}{\sinh x} = \frac{2}{e^x - e^{-x}}$$

$$\operatorname{sech} x = \frac{1}{\cosh x} = \frac{2}{e^x + e^{-x}}$$

$$\coth x = \frac{1}{\tanh x} = \frac{e^{2x} + 1}{e^{2x} - 1}$$

$$\cosh^2 x - \sinh^2 x = 1$$

$$\operatorname{sech}^2 x = 1 - \tanh^2 x$$

$$\operatorname{cosech}^2 x = \coth^2 x - 1$$

$$\sinh (x \pm y) = \sinh x \cosh y \pm \cosh x \sinh y$$

$$\cosh (x \pm y) = \cosh x \cosh y \pm \sinh x \sinh y$$

$$\tanh (x \pm y) = \frac{\tanh x \pm \tanh y}{1 \pm \tanh x \tanh y}$$

$$\operatorname{arc sinh} x = \log_e (x + \sqrt{x^2 + 1})$$

$$\operatorname{arc cosh} x = \pm\log_e (x + \sqrt{x^2 - 1})$$

$$\operatorname{arc tanh} x = \tfrac{1}{2} \log_e \frac{1 + x}{1 - x}$$

CALCULUS

Differentiation

Function	Derivative	Function	Derivative
ax^n	anx^{n-1}	$\sec x$	$\tan x \sec x$
$\sin ax$	$a \cos ax$	$\operatorname{cosec} x$	$-\cot x \operatorname{cosec} x$
$\cos ax$	$-a \sin ax$	$\arcsin x$	$(1 - x^2)^{-1/2}$
$\tan ax$	$a \sec^2 ax$	$\arccos x$	$-(1 - x^2)^{-1/2}$
$\log_e ax$	$\dfrac{1}{x}$	$\arctan x$	$(1 + x^2)^{-1}$
		$\operatorname{arc\,sinh} x$	$(1 + x^2)^{-1/2}$
e^{ax}	ae^{ax}	$\operatorname{arc\,cosh} x$	$(x^2 - 1)^{-1/2}$
$\cot x$	$-\operatorname{cosec}^2 x$	$\operatorname{arc\,tanh} x$	$(1 - x^2)^{-1}$

Product rule: if $y = uv$, $\dfrac{dy}{dx} = v\dfrac{du}{dx} + u\dfrac{dv}{dx}$ u and v are both functions of x

Quotient rule: if $y = \dfrac{u}{v}$, $\dfrac{dy}{dx} = \dfrac{v\dfrac{du}{dx} - u\dfrac{dv}{dx}}{v^2}$

Function of a function: $\dfrac{dy}{dx} = \dfrac{dy}{du} \times \dfrac{du}{dx}$

Conditions for maximum and minimum:

    y has a maximum value if $\dfrac{dy}{dx} = 0$ and $\dfrac{d^2y}{dx^2}$ is negative

    y has a minimum value if $\dfrac{dy}{dx} = 0$ and $\dfrac{d^2y}{dx^2}$ is positive

Point of inflexion: $\dfrac{d^2y}{dx^2}$ is zero and changes sign

If $z = f(x, y)$ then $\delta z = \dfrac{\partial z}{\partial x}\delta x + \dfrac{\partial z}{\partial y}\delta y$

If x and y are functions of t then $\dfrac{dz}{dt} = \dfrac{\partial z}{\partial x}\dfrac{dx}{dt} + \dfrac{\partial z}{\partial y}\dfrac{dy}{dt}$

Integration

Velocity and acceleration

If $s = f(t)$

$v = \dfrac{ds}{dt}$

$a = \dfrac{d^2s}{dt^2} = \dfrac{dv}{dt}$

s = distance travelled
v = velocity
a = acceleration

Function	Integral
x^n	$\dfrac{x^{n+1}}{n+1}$
$\dfrac{1}{x}$	$\log_e x$
e^x	e^x
$\log x$	$x \log x - x$
$\dfrac{1}{a^2 + x^2}$	$\dfrac{1}{a} \arctan \dfrac{x}{a}$
$\dfrac{1}{a^2 - x^2}$	$\dfrac{1}{2a} \log \dfrac{a+x}{a-x} = \dfrac{1}{a} \operatorname{arc\,tanh} \dfrac{x}{a}$
$\dfrac{1}{\sqrt{a^2 - x^2}}$	$\arcsin \dfrac{x}{a}$
$\dfrac{1}{\sqrt{x^2 + a^2}}$	$\operatorname{arc\,sinh} \dfrac{x}{a} = \log_e \left(\dfrac{x + \sqrt{x^2 + a^2}}{a} \right)$
$\dfrac{1}{\sqrt{x^2 - a^2}}$	$\operatorname{arc\,cosh} \dfrac{x}{a} = \log_e \left(\dfrac{x + \sqrt{x^2 - a^2}}{a} \right)$
$\sin x$	$-\cos x$
$\cos x$	$\sin x$
$\tan x$	$-\log \cos x$
$\cot x$	$\log \sin x$
$\sec x$	$\log \tan \left(\dfrac{\pi}{4} + \dfrac{x}{2} \right)$
$\operatorname{cosec} x$	$\log \tan \tfrac{1}{2}x$

Integration by parts

$$\int u \frac{dv}{dx}\, dx = uv - \int v \frac{du}{dx}\, dx \qquad u \text{ and } v \text{ are functions of } x$$

Fourier series

If $f(x) = a_0 + a_1 \cos x + a_2 \cos 2x + \ldots + b_1 \sin x + b_2 \sin 2x + \ldots$

then

$$a_0 = \frac{1}{2\pi} \int_{-\pi}^{\pi} f(x)\, dx$$

$$a_n = \frac{1}{\pi} \int_{-\pi}^{\pi} f(x) \cos nx\, dx$$

$$b_n = \frac{1}{\pi} \int_{-\pi}^{\pi} f(x) \sin nx\, dx$$

Area

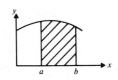

$$\text{Area } A = \int_a^b y\,dx$$

$$\text{Mean value} = \frac{1}{b-a}\int_a^b y\,dx$$

$$\text{Root mean square value (r.m.s.)} = \sqrt{\frac{1}{b-a}\int_a^b y^2\,dx}$$

Volume generated by rotating the area A completely about the x-axis is

$$\pi \int_a^b y^2\,dx.$$

Centroid of a plane area

$$\overline{x} = \frac{\displaystyle\int_a^b xy\,dx}{\text{area}} \qquad \overline{y} = \frac{\tfrac{1}{2}\displaystyle\int_a^b y^2\,dx}{\text{area}}$$

CENTROIDS OF SOME PLANE FIGURES

Rectangle

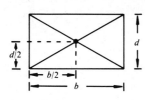

Centroid lies at the intersection of the diagonals.

Triangle

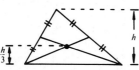

Centroid lies at the intersection of the bisectors of the sides.

Semi-circle

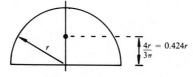

$$\frac{4r}{3\pi} = 0.424r$$

Quadrant of a circle

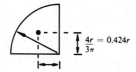

$$\frac{4r}{3\pi} = 0.424r$$

Segment of a circle

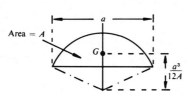

Area $= A$

$$\frac{a^3}{12A}$$

Sector of a circle	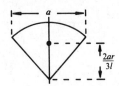	l = length of arc

Second moment of area

I (about y-axis) $= \int_a^b x^2 y \, dx$

$I = Ak^2$ where A is the area and k is the radius of gyration

Theorem of perpendicular axes

If OX and OY are two axes in the plane of a lamina and OZ is mutually perpendicular to OX and OY then

$$I_{OZ} = I_{OX} + I_{OY}$$

Theorem of parallel axes

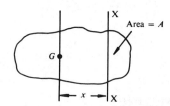

$$I_{XX} = I_G + Ax^2$$

Area = A

Pappus' theorem

Surface area of revolution $= 2\pi\bar{y}L$

Volume of revolution $\quad = 2\pi\bar{y}A$

Irregular plane areas

Mid-ordinate rule: Area $= b(h_1 + h_2 + h_3 + \dots h_n)$ $\quad$ see below

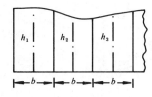 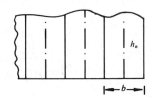

Trapezium (Trapezoidal) rule:

$$\text{Area} = \frac{b}{2}\left[(h_0 + h_n) + 2(h_1 + h_2 + \dots h_{n-1})\right] \quad \text{see below}$$

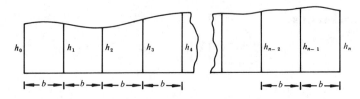

Simpson's rule:

$$\text{Area} = \frac{b}{3}\left[(h_0 + h_n) + 4(h_1 + h_3 + \dots h_{n-1}) + 2(h_2 + h_4 + \dots h_{n-2})\right]$$

(*n* must be even)

DIFFERENTIAL EQUATIONS

(1) $\dfrac{dy}{dx} = f(x)$, or $P\dfrac{dy}{dx} + Q = 0$, P and Q being functions of x only.

$P\dfrac{dy}{dx} + Q = 0$ can be written $\dfrac{dy}{dx} = -\dfrac{Q}{P} = f(x)$

Solution: $y = \displaystyle\int f(x)\, dx + c$

(2) $\dfrac{dy}{dx} = F(y)$, or $P\dfrac{dy}{dx} + Q = 0$, P and Q being functions of y only.

$P\dfrac{dy}{dx} + Q = 0$ can be written $\dfrac{dy}{dx} = -\dfrac{Q}{P} = F(y)$

Solution: $x = \displaystyle\int \dfrac{1}{F(y)}\, dy + c$

(3) $\dfrac{d^n y}{dx^n} = f(x)$, then $\dfrac{d^{n-1}y}{dx^{n-1}} = \displaystyle\int f(x)\, dx + c_1$

$$\dfrac{d^{n-2}y}{dx^{n-2}} = \displaystyle\int\left(\displaystyle\int f(x)\, dx + c_1\right)dx + c_2 \quad \text{etc.}$$

Solution: Obtained by continuous integration until y is obtained, each integration introduces an arbitrary constant.

(4) $P\dfrac{dy}{dx} + Q = 0$, where P is a function of y and Q is a function of x (or the equation can be written in this form).

Solution: $\displaystyle\int P\, dy = -\displaystyle\int Q\, dx + c$

(5) $P\dfrac{dy}{dx} + Q = 0$, P and Q being functions of x and y; if this can be written $P\, dy + Q\, dx = 0$, where the left hand side of the equation is an exact differential then $\dfrac{\partial Q}{\partial y} = \dfrac{\partial P}{\partial x}$

Solution: If the equation is exact the integral can be written down directly.

(6) $\dfrac{dy}{dx} + Py = Q$, where P and Q are functions of x only. This can be made exact by multiplying by the integrating factor $e^{\int P\, dx}$

Solution: Multiplying both sides of the equation by the integrating factor $e^{\int P\, dx}$. The left hand side will then be an exact differential and the right hand side can be integrated in the normal way.

(7) $\dfrac{d^2y}{dx^2} = f(y)$, this can be written $p\dfrac{dp}{dy} = f(y)$ by putting $p = \dfrac{dy}{dx}$

Solution: $\displaystyle\int p\, dp = \displaystyle\int f(y)\, dy + c$

(8) $\dfrac{d^2y}{dx^2} + a\dfrac{dy}{dx} + by = 0$, the solution depends on the form of the roots of the equation $k^2 + ak + b = 0$, called the auxiliary equation.

27

Solution:

(i) Roots of auxiliary equation real and different, say α and β

$$y = Ae^{\alpha x} + Be^{\beta x}$$

(ii) Roots of the auxiliary equation equal, say α

$$y = (Ax + B)e^{\alpha x}$$

(iii) Roots of the auxiliary equation complex, say $p + jq$, $p - jq$

$$y = e^{px}(C \cos qx + D \sin qx)$$

or $y = Re^{px} \sin(qx + \theta)$, where R and θ are the arbitrary constants.

(9) $\dfrac{d^2y}{dx^2} + a\dfrac{dy}{dx} + by = f(x)$

Solution: The general solution of this type of equation is made up of two parts, the complementary function, as above (8), and the particular integral, which depends on the $f(x)$ and can be found by using the D operator method.

Note: An alternative method of solution of this type of equation when the boundary conditions are given is to use Laplace transforms.

Definition: the Laplace transform of a function of t, say $F(t)$, is $\mathscr{L}\{F(t)\}$, where $\mathscr{L}\{F(t)\} = \displaystyle\int_0^\infty e^{-st}F(t)\, dt$.

Function	Laplace transform	Function	Laplace transform
1	$\dfrac{1}{s}$	t^n	$\dfrac{n!}{s^{n+1}}$
e^{at}	$\dfrac{1}{s-a}$	$\sinh at$	$\dfrac{a}{s^2 - a^2}$
$\sin at$	$\dfrac{a}{s^2 + a^2}$	$\cosh at$	$\dfrac{a}{s^2 - a^2}$
$\cos at$	$\dfrac{s}{s^2 + a^2}$	$e^{-at}t^n$	$\dfrac{n!}{(s+a)^{n+1}}$
t	$\dfrac{1}{s^2}$	$e^{-at}\cos at$	$\dfrac{s+b}{(s+b)^2 + a^2}$

Special cases

(10) $\dfrac{d^2y}{dx^2} = k_1 + k_2 x + k_3 x^2 + k_4 x^3 + \ldots + k_{n-1}x^{n-2}$

Solution: $y = k + k_0 x + k_1\dfrac{x^2}{1 \times 2} + k_2\dfrac{x^3}{2 \times 3} + \ldots + k_{n-1}\dfrac{x^n}{n(n-1)}$

This equation is used in the deflection of beams.

(11) $\dfrac{d^2y}{dt^2} + \omega^2 y = 0$, simple harmonic motion

y is the distance moved in time t and ω is the frequency in hertz.

Solution: $y = y_0 \sin(\omega t + \alpha)$ y_0 is the amplitude and α is the phase angle.

(12) $\dfrac{d^2y}{dt^2} + 2k\dfrac{dy}{dt} + \omega^2 y = 0$, damped vibrations. $2k$ is the damping coefficient.

Solution: $k < \omega$, $y = y_0\,e^{-kt}\sin\left(\sqrt{\omega^2 - k^2}\ldots t + \alpha\right)$

$k = \omega$, $y = (A + Bt)\,e^{-kt}$

$k > \omega$, $y = e^{-kt}\left(Ae^{\sqrt{k^2 - \omega^2}}\ldots t + Be^{\sqrt{-k^2 - \omega^2}}\ldots t\right)$

DETERMINANTS

If a, b, c and d are any four numbers then

$$\Delta = \begin{vmatrix} a & b \\ c & d \end{vmatrix} = ad - bc$$

Δ is called the determinant of order 2.

The determinant of order 3

$$\Delta = \begin{vmatrix} a_{11} & a_{12} & a_{13} \\ a_{21} & a_{22} & a_{23} \\ a_{31} & a_{32} & a_{33} \end{vmatrix} = a_{11}\begin{vmatrix} a_{22} & a_{23} \\ a_{32} & a_{33} \end{vmatrix} - a_{12}\begin{vmatrix} a_{21} & a_{23} \\ a_{31} & a_{33} \end{vmatrix} + a_{13}\begin{vmatrix} a_{21} & a_{22} \\ a_{31} & a_{32} \end{vmatrix}$$

$$= a_{11}(a_{22}a_{33} - a_{23}a_{32}) - a_{12}(a_{21}a_{33} - a_{23}a_{31}) + a_{13}(a_{21}a_{32} - a_{22}a_{31})$$

Minor The minor of an element a_{ij} is the determinant of order $(n - 1)$ formed from Δ by omitting the row and column containing a_{ij}.

Cofactor The cofactor of an element a_{ij} is its minor with the sign $+$ or $-$ according to the formula

$$A_{ij} = (-1)^{i+j} \times (\text{minor of } a_{ij})$$

Value of a determinant The value of a determinant of order n is

$$\Delta = a_{11}A_{11} + a_{12}A_{12} + a_{13}A_{13} + \ldots + a_{1n}A_{1n}$$

Using determinants to solve equations To solve the equations

$$a_{11}x_1 + a_{12}x_2 + \ldots + a_{1n}x_n = b_1$$
$$a_{21}x_1 + a_{22}x_2 + \ldots + a_{2n}x_n = b_2$$
$$\vdots \qquad \vdots \qquad \vdots \qquad \vdots \qquad \vdots$$
$$a_{n1}x_1 + a_{n2}x_2 + \ldots + a_{nn}x_n = b_n$$

$$\text{Let } \Delta = \begin{vmatrix} a_{11} & a_{12} & \cdots & a_{1n} \\ a_{21} & a_{22} & \cdots & a_{2n} \\ \vdots & \vdots & \vdots & \vdots \\ a_{n1} & a_{n2} & \cdots & a_{nn} \end{vmatrix}$$

$$\text{then } \Delta\,x_j = \begin{vmatrix} a_{11} & a_{12} & \cdots & a_{ij-1} & b_1 & a_{ij+1} & \cdots & a_{1n} \\ a_{21} & a_{22} & \cdots & a_{2i-1} & b_2 & a_{2j+1} & \cdots & a_{2n} \\ \vdots & \vdots & \vdots & \vdots & \vdots & \vdots & \vdots & \vdots \\ a_{n1} & a_{n2} & \cdots & a_{nj-1} & b_n & a_{nj+1} & \cdots & a_{nn} \end{vmatrix}$$

This method of solving linear equations is recommended only for small values of n.

MATRICES

A matrix which has an array of $m \times n$ numbers arranged in m rows and n columns is called an $m \times n$ matrix. It is denoted by

$$\begin{pmatrix} a_{11} & a_{12} & \cdots & a_{1n} \\ a_{21} & a_{22} & \cdots & a_{2n} \\ \vdots & \vdots & \vdots & \vdots \\ a_{m1} & a_{m1} & \cdots & a_{mn} \end{pmatrix}$$

Row matrix

This is a matrix having only 1 row. Thus $(a_{11}\, a_{12} \ldots a_{1n})$ is a row matrix of order $1 \times n$.

Column matrix

This is a matrix having only 1 column. Thus:

$$\begin{pmatrix} a_{11} \\ a_{21} \\ \vdots \\ a_{m1} \end{pmatrix}$$ is a column matrix of order $m \times 1$.

Null matrix

This is a matrix with all its elements zero.

$$\begin{pmatrix} 0 & 0 \\ 0 & 0 \end{pmatrix}$$ is a null matrix of order 2×2.

Square matrix

This is a matrix having the same number of rows and columns.

$$\begin{pmatrix} a_{11} & a_{12} & a_{13} \\ a_{21} & a_{22} & a_{23} \\ a_{31} & a_{32} & a_{33} \end{pmatrix}$$ is a square matrix of order 3×3.

Diagonal matrix

This is a square matrix in which all the elements are zero except those in the leading diagonal.

$$\begin{pmatrix} a_{11} & 0 & 0 \\ 0 & a_{22} & 0 \\ 0 & 0 & a_{33} \end{pmatrix}$$ is a diagonal matrix of order 3×3.

Unit matrix

This is a diagonal matrix with the elements in the leading diagonal all equal to 1. All other elements are 0. The unit matrix is denoted by I.

$$I = \begin{pmatrix} 1 & 0 & 0 \\ 0 & 1 & 0 \\ 0 & 0 & 1 \end{pmatrix}$$

Addition of matrices

Two matrices may be added provided that they are of the same order. This is done by adding the corresponding elements in each matrix.

$$\begin{pmatrix} a_{11} & a_{12} & a_{13} \\ a_{21} & a_{22} & a_{23} \end{pmatrix} + \begin{pmatrix} b_{11} & b_{12} & b_{13} \\ b_{21} & b_{22} & b_{23} \end{pmatrix} = \begin{pmatrix} a_{11}+b_{11} & a_{12}+b_{12} & a_{13}+b_{13} \\ a_{21}+b_{21} & a_{22}+b_{22} & a_{23}+b_{23} \end{pmatrix}$$

Subtraction of matrices

Subtraction is done in a similar way to addition except that the corresponding elements are subtracted.

$$\begin{pmatrix} a_{11} & a_{12} \\ a_{21} & a_{22} \end{pmatrix} - \begin{pmatrix} b_{11} & b_{12} \\ b_{21} & b_{22} \end{pmatrix} = \begin{pmatrix} a_{11}-b_{11} & a_{12}-b_{12} \\ a_{21}-b_{21} & a_{22}-b_{22} \end{pmatrix}$$

| **Scalar multiplication** | A matrix may be multiplied by a number as follows: |

$$b \begin{pmatrix} a_{11} & a_{12} \\ a_{21} & a_{22} \end{pmatrix} = \begin{pmatrix} ba_{11} & ba_{12} \\ ba_{21} & ba_{22} \end{pmatrix}$$

| **General matrix multiplication** | Two matrices can be multiplied together provided the number of columns in the first matrix is equal to the number of rows in the second matrix. |

$$\begin{pmatrix} a_{11} & a_{12} & a_{13} \\ a_{21} & a_{22} & a_{23} \end{pmatrix} \begin{pmatrix} b_{11} & b_{12} \\ b_{21} & b_{22} \\ b_{31} & b_{32} \end{pmatrix}$$

$$= \begin{pmatrix} a_{11}b_{11} + a_{12}b_{21} + a_{13}b_{31} & a_{11}b_{12} + a_{12}b_{22} + a_{13}b_{32} \\ a_{21}b_{11} + a_{22}b_{21} + a_{23}b_{31} & a_{21}b_{12} + a_{22}b_{22} + a_{23}b_{32} \end{pmatrix}$$

If matrix A is of order $(p \times q)$ and matrix B is of order $(q \times r)$ then if $C = AB$ the order of C is $(p \times r)$.

| **Transposition of a matrix** | When the rows of a matrix are interchanged with its columns the matrix is said to be transposed. If the original matrix is denoted by A, its transpose is denoted by A' or A^T. |

$$\text{If } A = \begin{pmatrix} a_{11} & a_{12} & a_{13} \\ a_{21} & a_{22} & a_{23} \end{pmatrix} \quad \text{then} \quad A^T = \begin{pmatrix} a_{11} & a_{21} \\ a_{12} & a_{22} \\ a_{13} & a_{23} \end{pmatrix}$$

| **Adjoint of a matrix** | If $A = [a_{ij}]$ is any matrix and A_{ij} is the cofactor of a_{ij}, the matrix $[A_{ij}]^T$ is called the adjoint of A. Thus: |

$$A = \begin{pmatrix} a_{11} & a_{12} & \cdots & a_{1n} \\ a_{21} & a_{22} & \cdots & a_{2n} \\ \vdots & \vdots & \vdots & \vdots \\ a_{n1} & a_{n2} & \cdots & a_{nn} \end{pmatrix} \quad \text{adj } A = \begin{pmatrix} A_{11} & A_{21} & \cdots & A_{n1} \\ A_{12} & A_{22} & \cdots & A_{n2} \\ \vdots & \vdots & \vdots & \vdots \\ A_{1n} & A_{2n} & \cdots & A_{nn} \end{pmatrix}$$

| **Singular matrix** | A square matrix is singular if the determinant of its coefficients is zero. |

| **The inverse of a matrix** | If A is a non-singular matrix of order $(n \times n)$ then its inverse is denoted by A^{-1} such that $AA^{-1} = I = A^{-1}A$ |

$$A^{-1} = \frac{\text{adj } (A)}{\Delta} \qquad \Delta = \det (A)$$
$$A_{ij} = \text{cofactor of } a_{ij}$$

$$\text{If } A = \begin{pmatrix} a_{11} & a_{12} & \cdots & a_{1n} \\ a_{21} & a_{22} & \cdots & a_{2n} \\ \vdots & \vdots & \vdots & \vdots \\ a_{n1} & a_{n2} & \cdots & a_{nn} \end{pmatrix} \quad A^{-1} = \frac{1}{\Delta} \begin{pmatrix} A_{11} & A_{21} & \cdots & A_{n1} \\ A_{12} & A_{22} & \cdots & A_{n2} \\ \vdots & \vdots & \vdots & \vdots \\ A_{1n} & A_{2n} & \cdots & A_{nn} \end{pmatrix}$$

| **Solutions of linear equations** | The set of linear equations |

$$\begin{aligned} a_{11}x_1 + \quad a_{12}x_2 + \quad &\cdots \quad a_{1n}x_n = b_1 \\ a_{21}x_1 + \quad a_{22}x_2 + \quad &\cdots \quad a_{2n}x_n = b_2 \\ \vdots \qquad \vdots \qquad &\vdots \qquad \vdots \\ a_{n1}x_1 + \quad a_{n2}x_2 + \quad &\cdots \quad a_{nn}x_n = b_n \end{aligned}$$

may be written in matrix form as $Ax = b$

If A is non-singular then the solution is given by $x = A^{-1}b$.

NATURAL SINES

°	0' 0.0°	6' 0.1°	12' 0.2°	18' 0.3°	24' 0.4°	30' 0.5°	36' 0.6°	42' 0.7°	48' 0.8°	54' 0.9°	1'	2'	3'	4'	5'
0	0.0000	0.0017	0.0035	0.0052	0.0070	0.0087	0.0105	0.0122	0.0140	0.0157	3	6	9	12	15
1	0.0175	0.0192	0.0209	0.0227	0.0244	0.0262	0.0279	0.0297	0.0314	0.0332	3	6	9	12	15
2	0.0349	0.0366	0.0384	0.0401	0.0419	0.0436	0.0454	0.0471	0.0488	0.0506	3	6	9	12	15
3	0.0523	0.0541	0.0558	0.0576	0.0593	0.0610	0.0628	0.0645	0.0663	0.0680	3	6	9	12	15
4	0.0698	0.0715	0.0732	0.0750	0.0767	0.0785	0.0802	0.0819	0.0837	0.0854	3	6	9	12	14
5	0.0872	0.0889	0.0906	0.0924	0.0941	0.0958	0.0976	0.0993	0.1011	0.1028	3	6	9	12	14
6	0.1045	0.1063	0.1080	0.1097	0.1115	0.1132	0.1149	0.1167	0.1184	0.1201	3	6	9	12	14
7	0.1219	0.1236	0.1253	0.1271	0.1288	0.1305	0.1323	0.1340	0.1357	0.1374	3	6	9	12	14
8	0.1392	0.1409	0.1426	0.1444	0.1461	0.1478	0.1495	0.1513	0.1530	0.1547	3	6	9	11	14
9	0.1564	0.1582	0.1599	0.1616	0.1633	0.1650	0.1668	0.1685	0.1702	0.1719	3	6	9	11	14
10	0.1736	0.1754	0.1771	0.1788	0.1805	0.1822	0.1840	0.1857	0.1874	0.1891	3	6	9	11	14
11	0.1908	0.1925	0.1942	0.1959	0.1977	0.1994	0.2011	0.2028	0.2045	0.2062	3	6	9	11	14
12	0.2079	0.2096	0.2113	0.2130	0.2147	0.2164	0.2181	0.2198	0.2215	0.2232	3	6	9	11	14
13	0.2250	0.2267	0.2284	0.2300	0.2317	0.2334	0.2351	0.2368	0.2385	0.2402	3	6	8	11	14
14	0.2419	0.2436	0.2453	0.2470	0.2487	0.2504	0.2521	0.2538	0.2554	0.2571	3	6	8	11	14
15	0.2588	0.2605	0.2622	0.2639	0.2656	0.2672	0.2689	0.2706	0.2723	0.2740	3	6	8	11	14
16	0.2756	0.2773	0.2790	0.2807	0.2823	0.2840	0.2857	0.2874	0.2890	0.2907	3	6	8	11	14
17	0.2924	0.2940	0.2957	0.2974	0.2990	0.3007	0.3024	0.3040	0.3057	0.3074	3	6	8	11	14
18	0.3090	0.3107	0.3123	0.3140	0.3156	0.3173	0.3190	0.3206	0.3223	0.3239	3	6	8	11	14
19	0.3256	0.3272	0.3289	0.3305	0.3322	0.3338	0.3355	0.3371	0.3387	0.3404	3	5	8	11	14
20	0.3420	0.3437	0.3453	0.3469	0.3486	0.3502	0.3518	0.3535	0.3551	0.3567	3	5	8	11	14
21	0.3584	0.3600	0.3616	0.3633	0.3649	0.3665	0.3681	0.3697	0.3714	0.3730	3	5	8	11	14
22	0.3746	0.3762	0.3778	0.3795	0.3811	0.3827	0.3843	0.3859	0.3875	0.3891	3	5	8	11	13
23	0.3907	0.3923	0.3939	0.3955	0.3971	0.3987	0.4003	0.4019	0.4035	0.4051	3	5	8	11	13
24	0.4067	0.4083	0.4099	0.4115	0.4131	0.4147	0.4163	0.4179	0.4195	0.4210	3	5	8	11	13
25	0.4226	0.4242	0.4258	0.4274	0.4289	0.4305	0.4321	0.4337	0.4352	0.4368	3	5	8	11	13
26	0.4384	0.4399	0.4415	0.4431	0.4446	0.4462	0.4478	0.4493	0.4509	0.4524	3	5	8	10	13
27	0.4540	0.4555	0.4571	0.4586	0.4602	0.4617	0.4633	0.4648	0.4664	0.4679	3	5	8	10	13
28	0.4695	0.4710	0.4726	0.4741	0.4756	0.4772	0.4787	0.4802	0.4818	0.4833	3	5	8	10	13
29	0.4848	0.4863	0.4879	0.4894	0.4909	0.4924	0.4939	0.4955	0.4970	0.4985	3	5	8	10	13
30	0.5000	0.5015	0.5030	0.5045	0.5060	0.5075	0.5090	0.5105	0.5120	0.5135	3	5	8	10	13
31	0.5150	0.5165	0.5180	0.5195	0.5210	0.5225	0.5240	0.5255	0.5270	0.5284	2	5	7	10	12
32	0.5299	0.5314	0.5329	0.5344	0.5358	0.5373	0.5388	0.5402	0.5417	0.5432	2	5	7	10	12
33	0.5446	0.5461	0.5476	0.5490	0.5505	0.5519	0.5534	0.5548	0.5563	0.5577	2	5	7	10	12
34	0.5592	0.5606	0.5621	0.5635	0.5650	0.5664	0.5678	0.5693	0.5707	0.5721	2	5	7	10	12
35	0.5736	0.5750	0.5764	0.5779	0.5793	0.5807	0.5821	0.5835	0.5850	0.5864	2	5	7	9	12
36	0.5878	0.5892	0.5906	0.5920	0.5934	0.5948	0.5962	0.5976	0.5990	0.6004	2	5	7	9	12
37	0.6018	0.6032	0.6046	0.6060	0.6074	0.6088	0.6101	0.6115	0.6129	0.6143	2	5	7	9	12
38	0.6157	0.6170	0.6184	0.6198	0.6211	0.6225	0.6239	0.6252	0.6266	0.6280	2	5	7	9	11
39	0.6293	0.6307	0.6320	0.6334	0.6347	0.6361	0.6374	0.6388	0.6401	0.6414	2	4	7	9	11
40	0.6428	0.6441	0.6455	0.6468	0.6481	0.6494	0.6508	0.6521	0.6534	0.6547	2	4	7	9	11
41	0.6561	0.6574	0.6587	0.6600	0.6613	0.6626	0.6639	0.6652	0.6665	0.6678	2	4	7	9	11
42	0.6691	0.6704	0.6717	0.6730	0.6743	0.6756	0.6769	0.6782	0.6794	0.6807	2	4	6	9	11
43	0.6820	0.6833	0.6845	0.6858	0.6871	0.6884	0.6896	0.6909	0.6921	0.6934	2	4	6	8	11
44	0.6947	0.6959	0.6972	0.6984	0.6997	0.7009	0.7022	0.7034	0.7046	0.7059	2	4	6	8	10

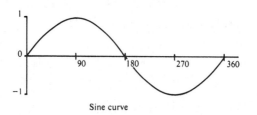

Sine curve

NATURAL SINES

°	0' 0.0°	6' 0.1°	12' 0.2°	18' 0.3°	24' 0.4°	30' 0.5°	36' 0.6°	42' 0.7°	48' 0.8°	54' 0.9°	1'	2'	3'	4'	5'
45	0.7071	0.7083	0.7096	0.7108	0.7120	0.7133	0.7145	0.7157	0.7169	0.7181	2	4	6	8	10
46	0.7193	0.7206	0.7218	0.7230	0.7242	0.7254	0.7266	0.7278	0.7290	0.7302	2	4	6	8	10
47	0.7314	0.7325	0.7337	0.7349	0.7361	0.7373	0.7385	0.7396	0.7408	0.7420	2	4	6	8	10
48	0.7431	0.7443	0.7455	0.7466	0.7478	0.7490	0.7501	0.7513	0.7524	0.7536	2	4	6	8	10
49	0.7547	0.7558	0.7570	0.7581	0.7593	0.7604	0.7615	0.7627	0.7638	0.7649	2	4	6	8	9
50	0.7660	0.7672	0.7683	0.7694	0.7705	0.7716	0.7727	0.7738	0.7749	0.7760	2	4	6	7	9
51	0.7771	0.7782	0.7793	0.7804	0.7815	0.7826	0.7837	0.7848	0.7859	0.7869	2	4	5	7	9
52	0.7880	0.7891	0.7902	0.7912	0.7923	0.7934	0.7944	0.7955	0.7965	0.7976	2	4	5	7	9
53	0.7986	0.7997	0.8007	0.8018	0.8028	0.8039	0.8049	0.8059	0.8070	0.8080	2	3	5	7	9
54	0.8090	0.8100	0.8111	0.8121	0.8131	0.8141	0.8151	0.8161	0.8171	0.8181	2	3	5	7	8
55	0.8192	0.8202	0.8211	0.8221	0.8231	0.8241	0.8251	0.8261	0.8271	0.8281	2	3	5	7	8
56	0.8290	0.8300	0.8310	0.8320	0.8329	0.8339	0.8348	0.8358	0.8368	0.8377	2	3	5	6	8
57	0.8387	0.8396	0.8406	0.8415	0.8425	0.8434	0.8443	0.8453	0.8462	0.8471	2	3	5	6	8
58	0.8480	0.8490	0.8499	0.8508	0.8517	0.8526	0.8536	0.8545	0.8554	0.8563	2	3	5	6	8
59	0.8572	0.8581	0.8590	0.8599	0.8607	0.8616	0.8625	0.8634	0.8643	0.8652	1	3	4	6	7
60	0.8660	0.8669	0.8678	0.8686	0.8695	0.8704	0.8712	0.8721	0.8729	0.8738	1	3	4	6	7
61	0.8746	0.8755	0.8763	0.8771	0.8780	0.8788	0.8796	0.8805	0.8813	0.8821	1	3	4	6	7
62	0.8829	0.8838	0.8846	0.8854	0.8862	0.8870	0.8878	0.8886	0.8894	0.8902	1	3	4	5	7
63	0.8910	0.8918	0.8926	0.8934	0.8942	0.8949	0.8957	0.8965	0.8973	0.8980	1	3	4	5	6
64	0.8988	0.8996	0.9003	0.9011	0.9018	0.9026	0.9033	0.9041	0.9048	0.9056	1	3	4	5	6
65	0.9063	0.9070	0.9078	0.9085	0.9092	0.9100	0.9107	0.9114	0.9121	0.9128	1	2	4	5	6
66	0.9135	0.9143	0.9150	0.9157	0.9164	0.9171	0.9178	0.9184	0.9191	0.9198	1	2	3	5	6
67	0.9205	0.9212	0.9219	0.9225	0.9232	0.9239	0.9245	0.9252	0.9259	0.9265	1	2	3	4	6
68	0.9272	0.9278	0.9285	0.9291	0.9298	0.9304	0.9311	0.9317	0.9323	0.9330	1	2	3	4	5
69	0.9336	0.9342	0.9348	0.9354	0.9361	0.9367	0.9373	0.9379	0.9385	0.9391	1	2	3	4	5
70	0.9397	0.9403	0.9409	0.9415	0.9421	0.9426	0.9432	0.9438	0.9444	0.9449	1	2	3	4	5
71	0.9455	0.9461	0.9466	0.9472	0.9478	0.9483	0.9489	0.9494	0.9500	0.9505	1	2	3	4	5
72	0.9511	0.9516	0.9521	0.9527	0.9532	0.9537	0.9542	0.9548	0.9553	0.9558	1	2	3	3	4
73	0.9563	0.9568	0.9573	0.9578	0.9583	0.9588	0.9593	0.9598	0.9603	0.9608	1	2	2	3	4
74	0.9613	0.9617	0.9622	0.9627	0.9632	0.9636	0.9641	0.9646	0.9650	0.9655	1	2	2	3	4
75	0.9659	0.9664	0.9668	0.9673	0.9677	0.9681	0.9686	0.9690	0.9694	0.9699	1	1	2	3	4
76	0.9703	0.9707	0.9711	0.9715	0.9720	0.9724	0.9728	0.9732	0.9736	0.9740	1	1	2	3	3
77	0.9744	0.9748	0.9751	0.9755	0.9759	0.9763	0.9767	0.9770	0.9774	0.9778	1	1	2	2	3
78	0.9781	0.9785	0.9789	0.9792	0.9796	0.9799	0.9803	0.9806	0.9810	0.9813	1	1	2	2	3
79	0.9816	0.9820	0.9823	0.9826	0.9829	0.9833	0.9836	0.9839	0.9842	0.9845	1	1	2	2	3
80	0.9848	0.9851	0.9854	0.9857	0.9860	0.9863	0.9866	0.9869	0.9871	0.9874	0	1	1	2	2
81	0.9877	0.9880	0.9882	0.9885	0.9888	0.9890	0.9893	0.9895	0.9898	0.9900	0	1	1	2	2
82	0.9903	0.9905	0.9907	0.9910	0.9912	0.9914	0.9917	0.9919	0.9921	0.9923	0	1	1	1	2
83	0.9925	0.9928	0.9930	0.9932	0.9934	0.9936	0.9938	0.9940	0.9942	0.9943	0	1	1	1	2
84	0.9945	0.9947	0.9949	0.9951	0.9952	0.9954	0.9956	0.9957	0.9959	0.9960	0	1	1	1	1
85	0.9962	0.9963	0.9965	0.9966	0.9968	0.9969	0.9971	0.9972	0.9973	0.9974	0	0	1	1	1
86	0.9976	0.9977	0.9978	0.9979	0.9980	0.9981	0.9982	0.9983	0.9984	0.9985	0	0	1	1	1
87	0.9986	0.9987	0.9988	0.9989	0.9990	0.9990	0.9991	0.9992	0.9993	0.9993	0	0	0	1	1
88	0.9994	0.9995	0.9995	0.9996	0.9996	0.9997	0.9997	0.9997	0.9998	0.9998	0	0	0	0	0
89	0.9998	0.9999	0.9999	0.9999	0.9999	1.0000	1.0000	1.0000	1.0000	1.0000	0	0	0	0	0
90	1.0000														

Quadrant	Angle	sin A =	Examples
first	0 to 90°	sin A	sin 34° 38' = 0.5683
second	90° to 180°	sin (180° − A)	sin 145° 22' = sin (180° − 145° 22')
third	180° to 270°	−sin (A − 180°)	= sin 34° 38' = 0.5683
fourth	270° to 360°	−sin (360° − A)	sin 214° 38' = −sin (214° 38' − 180°)
			= −sin 34° 38' = −0.5683
			sin 325° 22' = −sin (360° − 325° 22')
			= −sin 34° 38' = −0.5683

NATURAL COSINES Numbers in difference columns to be *subtracted*, not added.

°	0' 0.0°	6' 0.1°	12' 0.2°	18' 0.3°	24' 0.4°	30' 0.5°	36' 0.6°	42' 0.7°	48' 0.8°	54' 0.9°	1'	2'	3'	4'	5'
0	1.0000	1.0000	1.0000	1.0000	1.0000	1.0000	0.9999	0.9999	0.9999	0.9999	0	0	0	0	0
1	0.9998	0.9998	0.9998	0.9997	0.9997	0.9997	0.9996	0.9996	0.9995	0.9995	0	0	0	0	0
2	0.9994	0.9993	0.9993	0.9992	0.9991	0.9990	0.9990	0.9989	0.9988	0.9987	0	0	0	1	1
3	0.9986	0.9985	0.9984	0.9983	0.9982	0.9981	0.9980	0.9979	0.9978	0.9977	0	0	1	1	1
4	0.9976	0.9974	0.9973	0.9972	0.9971	0.9969	0.9968	0.9966	0.9965	0.9963	0	0	1	1	1
5	0.9962	0.9960	0.9959	0.9957	0.9956	0.9954	0.9952	0.9951	0.9949	0.9947	0	1	1	1	1
6	0.9945	0.9943	0.9942	0.9940	0.9938	0.9936	0.9934	0.9932	0.9930	0.9928	0	1	1	1	2
7	0.9925	0.9923	0.9921	0.9919	0.9917	0.9914	0.9912	0.9910	0.9907	0.9905	0	1	1	1	2
8	0.9903	0.9900	0.9898	0.9895	0.9893	0.9890	0.9888	0.9885	0.9882	0.9880	0	1	1	2	2
9	0.9877	0.9874	0.9871	0.9869	0.9866	0.9863	0.9860	0.9857	0.9854	0.9851	0	1	1	2	2
10	0.9848	0.9845	0.9842	0.9839	0.9836	0.9833	0.9829	0.9826	0.9823	0.9820	1	1	2	2	3
11	0.9816	0.9813	0.9810	0.9806	0.9803	0.9799	0.9796	0.9792	0.9789	0.9785	1	1	2	2	3
12	0.9781	0.9778	0.9774	0.9770	0.9767	0.9763	0.9759	0.9755	0.9751	0.9748	1	1	2	2	3
13	0.9744	0.9740	0.9736	0.9732	0.9728	0.9724	0.9720	0.9715	0.9711	0.9707	1	1	2	3	3
14	0.9703	0.9699	0.9694	0.9690	0.9686	0.9681	0.9677	0.9673	0.9668	0.9664	1	1	2	3	4
15	0.9659	0.9655	0.9650	0.9646	0.9641	0.9636	0.9632	0.9627	0.9622	0.9617	1	2	2	3	4
16	0.9613	0.9608	0.9603	0.9598	0.9593	0.9588	0.9583	0.9578	0.9573	0.9568	1	2	2	3	4
17	0.9563	0.9558	0.9553	0.9548	0.9542	0.9537	0.9532	0.9527	0.9521	0.9516	1	2	3	3	4
18	0.9511	0.9505	0.9500	0.9494	0.9489	0.9483	0.9478	0.9472	0.9466	0.9461	1	2	3	4	5
19	0.9455	0.9449	0.9444	0.9438	0.9432	0.9426	0.9421	0.9415	0.9409	0.9403	1	2	3	4	5
20	0.9397	0.9391	0.9385	0.9379	0.9373	0.9367	0.9361	0.9354	0.9348	0.9342	1	2	3	4	5
21	0.9336	0.9330	0.9323	0.9317	0.9311	0.9304	0.9298	0.9291	0.9285	0.9278	1	2	3	4	5
22	0.9272	0.9265	0.9259	0.9252	0.9245	0.9239	0.9232	0.9225	0.9219	0.9212	1	2	3	4	6
23	0.9205	0.9198	0.9191	0.9184	0.9178	0.9171	0.9164	0.9157	0.9150	0.9143	1	2	3	5	6
24	0.9135	0.9128	0.9121	0.9114	0.9107	0.9100	0.9092	0.9085	0.9078	0.9070	1	2	4	5	6
25	0.9063	0.9056	0.9048	0.9041	0.9033	0.9026	0.9018	0.9011	0.9003	0.8996	1	3	4	5	6
26	0.8988	0.8980	0.8973	0.8965	0.8957	0.8949	0.8942	0.8934	0.8926	0.8918	1	3	4	5	6
27	0.8910	0.8902	0.8894	0.8886	0.8878	0.8870	0.8862	0.8854	0.8846	0.8838	1	3	4	5	7
28	0.8829	0.8821	0.8813	0.8805	0.8796	0.8788	0.8780	0.8771	0.8763	0.8755	1	3	4	6	7
29	0.8746	0.8738	0.8729	0.8721	0.8712	0.8704	0.8695	0.8686	0.8678	0.8669	1	3	4	6	7
30	0.8660	0.8652	0.8643	0.8634	0.8625	0.8616	0.8607	0.8599	0.8590	0.8581	1	3	4	6	7
31	0.8572	0.8563	0.8554	0.8545	0.8536	0.8526	0.8517	0.8508	0.8499	0.8490	2	3	5	6	8
32	0.8480	0.8471	0.8462	0.8453	0.8443	0.8434	0.8425	0.8415	0.8406	0.8396	2	3	5	6	8
33	0.8387	0.8377	0.8368	0.8358	0.8348	0.8339	0.8329	0.8320	0.8310	0.8300	2	3	5	6	8
34	0.8290	0.8281	0.8271	0.8261	0.8251	0.8241	0.8231	0.8221	0.8211	0.8202	2	3	5	7	8
35	0.8192	0.8181	0.8171	0.8161	0.8151	0.8141	0.8131	0.8121	0.8111	0.8100	2	3	5	7	8
36	0.8090	0.8080	0.8070	0.8059	0.8049	0.8039	0.8028	0.8018	0.8007	0.7997	2	3	5	7	9
37	0.7986	0.7976	0.7965	0.7955	0.7944	0.7934	0.7923	0.7912	0.7902	0.7891	2	4	5	7	9
38	0.7880	0.7869	0.7859	0.7848	0.7837	0.7826	0.7815	0.7804	0.7793	0.7782	2	4	5	7	9
39	0.7771	0.7760	0.7749	0.7738	0.7727	0.7716	0.7705	0.7694	0.7683	0.7672	2	4	6	7	9
40	0.7660	0.7649	0.7638	0.7627	0.7615	0.7604	0.7593	0.7581	0.7570	0.7559	2	4	6	8	9
41	0.7547	0.7536	0.7524	0.7513	0.7501	0.7490	0.7478	0.7466	0.7455	0.7443	2	4	6	8	10
42	0.7431	0.7420	0.7408	0.7396	0.7385	0.7373	0.7361	0.7349	0.7337	0.7325	2	4	6	8	10
43	0.7314	0.7302	0.7290	0.7278	0.7266	0.7254	0.7242	0.7230	0.7218	0.7206	2	4	6	8	10
44	0.7193	0.7181	0.7169	0.7157	0.7145	0.7133	0.7120	0.7108	0.7096	0.7083	2	4	6	8	10

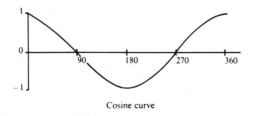

Cosine curve

NATURAL COSINES Numbers in difference columns to be *subtracted*, not added.

°	0' 0.0°	6' 0.1°	12' 0.2°	18' 0.3°	24' 0.4°	30' 0.5°	36' 0.6°	42' 0.7°	48' 0.8°	54' 0.9°	1'	2'	3'	4'	5'
45	0.7071	0.7059	0.7046	0.7034	0.7022	0.7009	0.6997	0.6984	0.6972	0.6959	2	4	6	8	10
46	0.6947	0.6934	0.6921	0.6909	0.6896	0.6884	0.6871	0.6858	0.6845	0.6833	2	4	6	8	11
47	0.6820	0.6807	0.6794	0.6782	0.6769	0.6756	0.6743	0.6730	0.6717	0.6704	2	4	6	9	11
48	0.6691	0.6678	0.6665	0.6652	0.6639	0.6626	0.6613	0.6600	0.6587	0.6574	2	4	7	9	11
49	0.6561	0.6547	0.6534	0.6521	0.6508	0.6494	0.6481	0.6468	0.6455	0.6441	2	4	7	9	11
50	0.6428	0.6414	0.6401	0.6388	0.6374	0.6361	0.6347	0.6334	0.6320	0.6307	2	4	7	9	11
51	0.6293	0.6280	0.6266	0.6252	0.6239	0.6225	0.6211	0.6198	0.6184	0.6170	2	5	7	9	11
52	0.6157	0.6143	0.6129	0.6115	0.6101	0.6088	0.6074	0.6060	0.6046	0.6032	2	5	7	9	12
53	0.6018	0.6004	0.5990	0.5976	0.5962	0.5948	0.5934	0.5920	0.5906	0.5892	2	5	7	9	12
54	0.5878	0.5864	0.5850	0.5835	0.5821	0.5807	0.5793	0.5779	0.5764	0.5750	2	5	7	9	12
55	0.5736	0.5721	0.5707	0.5693	0.5678	0.5664	0.5650	0.5635	0.5621	0.5606	2	5	7	10	12
56	0.5592	0.5577	0.5563	0.5548	0.5534	0.5519	0.5505	0.5490	0.5476	0.5461	2	5	7	10	12
57	0.5446	0.5432	0.5417	0.5402	0.5388	0.5373	0.5358	0.5344	0.5329	0.5314	2	5	7	10	12
58	0.5299	0.5284	0.5270	0.5255	0.5240	0.5225	0.5210	0.5195	0.5180	0.5165	2	5	7	10	12
59	0.5150	0.5135	0.5120	0.5105	0.5090	0.5075	0.5060	0.5045	0.5030	0.5015	3	5	8	10	13
60	0.5000	0.4985	0.4970	0.4955	0.4939	0.4924	0.4909	0.4894	0.4879	0.4863	3	5	8	10	13
61	0.4848	0.4833	0.4818	0.4802	0.4787	0.4772	0.4756	0.4741	0.4726	0.4710	3	5	8	10	13
62	0.4695	0.4679	0.4664	0.4648	0.4633	0.4617	0.4602	0.4586	0.4571	0.4555	3	5	8	10	13
63	0.4540	0.4524	0.4509	0.4493	0.4478	0.4462	0.4446	0.4431	0.4415	0.4399	3	5	8	10	13
64	0.4384	0.4368	0.4352	0.4337	0.4321	0.4305	0.4289	0.4274	0.4258	0.4242	3	5	8	11	13
65	0.4226	0.4210	0.4195	0.4179	0.4163	0.4147	0.4131	0.4115	0.4099	0.4083	3	5	8	11	13
66	0.4067	0.4051	0.4035	0.4019	0.4003	0.3987	0.3971	0.3955	0.3939	0.3923	3	5	8	11	13
67	0.3907	0.3891	0.3875	0.3859	0.3843	0.3827	0.3811	0.3795	0.3778	0.3762	3	5	8	11	13
68	0.3746	0.3730	0.3714	0.3697	0.3681	0.3665	0.3649	0.3633	0.3616	0.3600	3	5	8	11	14
69	0.3584	0.3567	0.3551	0.3535	0.3518	0.3502	0.3486	0.3469	0.3453	0.3437	3	5	8	11	14
70	0.3420	0.3404	0.3387	0.3371	0.3355	0.3338	0.3322	0.3305	0.3289	0.3272	3	5	8	11	14
71	0.3256	0.3239	0.3223	0.3206	0.3190	0.3173	0.3156	0.3140	0.3123	0.3107	3	6	8	11	14
72	0.3090	0.3074	0.3057	0.3040	0.3024	0.3007	0.2990	0.2974	0.2957	0.2940	3	6	8	11	14
73	0.2924	0.2907	0.2890	0.2874	0.2857	0.2840	0.2823	0.2807	0.2790	0.2773	3	6	8	11	14
74	0.2756	0.2740	0.2723	0.2706	0.2689	0.2672	0.2656	0.2639	0.2622	0.2605	3	6	8	11	14
75	0.2588	0.2571	0.2554	0.2538	0.2521	0.2504	0.2487	0.2470	0.2453	0.2436	3	6	8	11	14
76	0.2419	0.2402	0.2385	0.2368	0.2351	0.2334	0.2317	0.2300	0.2284	0.2267	3	6	8	11	14
77	0.2250	0.2233	0.2215	0.2198	0.2181	0.2164	0.2147	0.2130	0.2113	0.2096	3	6	9	11	14
78	0.2079	0.2062	0.2045	0.2028	0.2011	0.1994	0.1977	0.1959	0.1942	0.1925	3	6	9	11	14
79	0.1908	0.1891	0.1874	0.1857	0.1840	0.1822	0.1805	0.1788	0.1771	0.1754	3	6	9	11	14
80	0.1736	0.1719	0.1702	0.1685	0.1668	0.1650	0.1633	0.1616	0.1599	0.1582	3	6	9	11	14
81	0.1564	0.1547	0.1530	0.1513	0.1495	0.1478	0.1461	0.1444	0.1426	0.1409	3	6	9	11	14
82	0.1392	0.1374	0.1357	0.1340	0.1323	0.1305	0.1288	0.1271	0.1253	0.1236	3	6	9	12	14
83	0.1219	0.1201	0.1184	0.1167	0.1149	0.1132	0.1115	0.1097	0.1080	0.1063	3	6	9	12	14
84	0.1045	0.1028	0.1011	0.0993	0.0976	0.0958	0.0941	0.0924	0.0906	0.0889	3	6	9	12	14
85	0.0872	0.0854	0.0837	0.0819	0.0802	0.0785	0.0767	0.0750	0.0732	0.0715	3	6	9	12	14
86	0.0698	0.0680	0.0663	0.0645	0.0628	0.0610	0.0593	0.0576	0.0558	0.0541	3	6	9	12	15
87	0.0523	0.0506	0.0488	0.0471	0.0454	0.0436	0.0419	0.0401	0.0384	0.0366	3	6	9	12	15
88	0.0349	0.0332	0.0314	0.0297	0.0279	0.0262	0.0244	0.0227	0.0209	0.0192	3	6	9	12	15
89	0.0175	0.0157	0.0140	0.0122	0.0105	0.0087	0.0070	0.0052	0.0035	0.0017	3	6	9	12	15
90	0.0000														

Quadrant	Angle	cos A =	Examples
first	0 to 90°	cos A	cos 33° 26' = 0.8345
second	90° to 180°	$-\cos(180° - A)$	cos 146° 34' = $-\cos(180° - 146° 34')$
third	180° to 270°	$-\cos(A - 180°)$	= $-\cos 33° 26' = -0.8345$
fourth	270° to 360°	$\cos(360° - A)$	cos 213° 26' = $-\cos(213° 26' - 180°)$
			= $-\cos 33° 26' = -0.8345$
			cos 326° 34' = $\cos(360° - 326° 34')$
			= $\cos 33° 26' = 0.8345$

NATURAL TANGENTS

°	0' 0.0°	6' 0.1°	12' 0.2°	18' 0.3°	24' 0.4°	30' 0.5°	36' 0.6°	42' 0.7°	48' 0.8°	54' 0.9°	1'	2'	3'	4'	5'
0	0.0000	0.0017	0.0035	0.0052	0.0070	0.0087	0.0105	0.0122	0.0140	0.0157	3	6	9	12	15
1	0.0175	0.0192	0.0209	0.0227	0.0244	0.0262	0.0279	0.0297	0.0314	0.0332	3	6	9	12	15
2	0.0349	0.0367	0.0384	0.0402	0.0419	0.0437	0.0454	0.0472	0.0489	0.0507	3	6	9	12	15
3	0.0524	0.0542	0.0559	0.0577	0.0594	0.0612	0.0629	0.0647	0.0664	0.0682	3	6	9	12	15
4	0.0699	0.0717	0.0734	0.0752	0.0769	0.0787	0.0805	0.0822	0.0840	0.0857	3	6	9	12	15
5	0.0875	0.0892	0.0910	0.0928	0.0945	0.0963	0.0981	0.0998	0.1016	0.1033	3	6	9	12	15
6	0.1051	0.1069	0.1086	0.1104	0.1122	0.1139	0.1157	0.1175	0.1192	0.1210	3	6	9	12	15
7	0.1228	0.1246	0.1263	0.1281	0.1299	0.1317	0.1334	0.1352	0.1370	0.1388	3	6	9	12	15
8	0.1405	0.1423	0.1441	0.1459	0.1477	0.1495	0.1512	0.1530	0.1548	0.1566	3	6	9	12	15
9	0.1584	0.1602	0.1620	0.1638	0.1655	0.1673	0.1691	0.1709	0.1727	0.1745	3	6	9	12	15
10	0.1763	0.1781	0.1799	0.1817	0.1835	0.1853	0.1871	0.1890	0.1908	0.1926	3	6	9	12	15
11	0.1944	0.1962	0.1980	0.1998	0.2016	0.2035	0.2053	0.2071	0.2089	0.2107	3	6	9	12	15
12	0.2126	0.2144	0.2162	0.2180	0.2199	0.2217	0.2235	0.2254	0.2272	0.2290	3	6	9	12	15
13	0.2309	0.2327	0.2345	0.2364	0.2382	0.2401	0.2419	0.2438	0.2456	0.2475	3	6	9	12	15
14	0.2493	0.2512	0.2530	0.2549	0.2568	0.2586	0.2605	0.2623	0.2642	0.2661	3	6	9	12	16
15	0.2679	0.2698	0.2717	0.2736	0.2754	0.2773	0.2792	0.2811	0.2830	0.2849	3	6	9	13	16
16	0.2867	0.2886	0.2905	0.2924	0.2943	0.2962	0.2981	0.3000	0.3019	0.3038	3	6	9	13	16
17	0.3057	0.3076	0.3096	0.3115	0.3134	0.3153	0.3172	0.3191	0.3211	0.3230	3	6	10	13	16
18	0.3249	0.3269	0.3288	0.3307	0.3327	0.3346	0.3365	0.3385	0.3404	0.3424	3	6	10	13	16
19	0.3443	0.3463	0.3482	0.3502	0.3522	0.3541	0.3561	0.3581	0.3600	0.3620	3	7	10	13	16
20	0.3640	0.3659	0.3679	0.3699	0.3719	0.3739	0.3759	0.3779	0.3799	0.3819	3	7	10	13	17
21	0.3839	0.3859	0.3879	0.3899	0.3919	0.3939	0.3959	0.3979	0.4000	0.4020	3	7	10	13	17
22	0.4040	0.4061	0.4081	0.4101	0.4122	0.4142	0.4163	0.4183	0.4204	0.4224	3	7	10	14	17
23	0.4245	0.4265	0.4286	0.4307	0.4327	0.4348	0.4369	0.4390	0.4411	0.4431	3	7	10	14	17
24	0.4452	0.4473	0.4494	0.4515	0.4536	0.4557	0.4578	0.4599	0.4621	0.4642	4	7	11	14	18
25	0.4663	0.4684	0.4706	0.4727	0.4748	0.4770	0.4791	0.4813	0.4834	0.4856	4	7	11	14	18
26	0.4877	0.4899	0.4921	0.4942	0.4964	0.4986	0.5008	0.5029	0.5051	0.5073	4	7	11	15	18
27	0.5095	0.5117	0.5139	0.5161	0.5184	0.5206	0.5228	0.5250	0.5272	0.5295	4	7	11	15	18
28	0.5317	0.5340	0.5362	0.5384	0.5407	0.5430	0.5452	0.5475	0.5498	0.5520	4	8	11	15	19
29	0.5543	0.5566	0.5589	0.5612	0.5635	0.5658	0.5681	0.5704	0.5727	0.5750	4	8	12	15	19
30	0.5774	0.5797	0.5820	0.5844	0.5867	0.5890	0.5914	0.5938	0.5961	0.5985	4	8	12	16	20
31	0.6009	0.6032	0.6056	0.6080	0.6104	0.6128	0.6152	0.6176	0.6200	0.6224	4	8	12	16	20
32	0.6249	0.6273	0.6297	0.6322	0.6346	0.6371	0.6395	0.6420	0.6445	0.6469	4	8	12	16	20
33	0.6494	0.6519	0.6544	0.6569	0.6594	0.6619	0.6644	0.6669	0.6694	0.6720	4	8	13	17	21
34	0.6745	0.6771	0.6796	0.6822	0.6847	0.6873	0.6899	0.6924	0.6950	0.6976	4	9	13	17	21
35	0.7002	0.7028	0.7054	0.7080	0.7107	0.7133	0.7159	0.7186	0.7212	0.7239	4	9	13	17	22
36	0.7265	0.7292	0.7319	0.7346	0.7373	0.7400	0.7427	0.7454	0.7481	0.7508	5	9	14	18	23
37	0.7536	0.7563	0.7590	0.7618	0.7646	0.7673	0.7701	0.7729	0.7757	0.7785	5	9	14	18	23
38	0.7813	0.7841	0.7869	0.7898	0.7926	0.7954	0.7983	0.8012	0.8040	0.8069	5	9	14	19	24
39	0.8098	0.8127	0.8156	0.8185	0.8214	0.8243	0.8273	0.8302	0.8332	0.8361	5	10	15	20	24
40	0.8391	0.8421	0.8451	0.8481	0.8511	0.8541	0.8571	0.8601	0.8632	0.8662	5	10	15	20	25
41	0.8693	0.8724	0.8754	0.8785	0.8816	0.8847	0.8878	0.8910	0.8941	0.8972	5	10	16	21	26
42	0.9004	0.9036	0.9067	0.9099	0.9131	0.9163	0.9195	0.9228	0.9260	0.9293	5	11	16	21	27
43	0.9325	0.9358	0.9391	0.9424	0.9457	0.9490	0.9523	0.9556	0.9590	0.9623	6	11	17	22	28
44	0.9657	0.9691	0.9725	0.9759	0.9793	0.9827	0.9861	0.9896	0.9930	0.9965	6	11	17	23	28

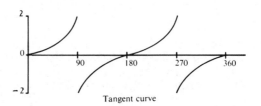

Tangent curve

NATURAL TANGENTS

°	0' 0.0°	6' 0.1°	12' 0.2°	18' 0.3°	24' 0.4°	30' 0.5°	36' 0.6°	42' 0.7°	48' 0.8°	54' 0.9°	1'	2'	3'	4'	5'
45	1.0000	1.0035	1.0070	1.0105	1.0141	1.0176	1.0212	1.0247	1.0283	1.0319	6	12	18	24	30
46	1.0355	1.0392	1.0428	1.0464	1.0501	1.0538	1.0575	1.0612	1.0649	1.0686	6	12	18	25	31
47	1.0724	1.0761	1.0799	1.0837	1.0875	1.0913	1.0951	1.0990	1.1028	1.1067	6	13	19	25	32
48	1.1106	1.1145	1.1184	1.1224	1.1263	1.1303	1.1343	1.1383	1.1423	1.1463	7	13	20	27	33
49	1.1504	1.1544	1.1585	1.1626	1.1667	1.1708	1.1750	1.1792	1.1833	1.1875	7	14	21	28	34
50	1.1918	1.1960	1.2002	1.2045	1.2088	1.2131	1.2174	1.2218	1.2261	1.2305	7	14	22	29	36
51	1.2349	1.2393	1.2437	1.2482	1.2527	1.2572	1.2617	1.2662	1.2708	1.2753	8	15	23	30	38
52	1.2799	1.2846	1.2892	1.2938	1.2985	1.3032	1.3079	1.3127	1.3175	1.3222	8	16	24	31	39
53	1.3270	1.3319	1.3367	1.3416	1.3465	1.3514	1.3564	1.3613	1.3663	1.3713	8	16	25	33	41
54	1.3764	1.3814	1.3865	1.3916	1.3968	1.4019	1.4071	1.4124	1.4176	1.4229	9	17	26	34	43
55	1.4281	1.4335	1.4388	1.4442	1.4496	1.4550	1.4605	1.4659	1.4715	1.4770	9	18	27	36	45
56	1.4826	1.4882	1.4938	1.4994	1.5051	1.5108	1.5166	1.5224	1.5282	1.5340	10	19	29	38	48
57	1.5399	1.5458	1.5517	1.5577	1.5637	1.5697	1.5757	1.5818	1.5880	1.5941	10	20	30	40	50
58	1.6003	1.6066	1.6128	1.6191	1.6255	1.6319	1.6383	1.6447	1.6512	1.6577	11	21	32	43	53
59	1.6643	1.6709	1.6775	1.6842	1.6909	1.6977	1.7045	1.7113	1.7182	1.7251	11	23	34	45	56
60	1.7321	1.7391	1.7461	1.7532	1.7603	1.7675	1.7747	1.7820	1.7893	1.7966	12	24	36	48	60
61	1.8040	1.8115	1.8190	1.8265	1.8341	1.8418	1.8495	1.8572	1.8650	1.8728	13	26	38	51	64
62	1.8807	1.8887	1.8967	1.9047	1.9128	1.9210	1.9292	1.9375	1.9458	1.9542	14	27	41	55	68
63	1.9626	1.9711	1.9797	1.9883	1.9970	2.0057	2.0145	2.0233	2.0323	2.0413	15	29	44	58	73
64	2.0503	2.0594	2.0686	2.0778	2.0872	2.0965	2.1060	2.1155	2.1251	2.1348	16	31	47	63	78
65	2.1445	2.1543	2.1642	2.1742	2.1842	2.1943	2.2045	2.2148	2.2251	2.2355	17	34	51	68	85
66	2.2460	2.2566	2.2673	2.2781	2.2889	2.2998	2.3109	2.3220	2.3332	2.3445	18	37	55	73	92
67	2.3559	2.3673	2.3789	2.3906	2.4023	2.4142	2.4262	2.4383	2.4504	2.4627	20	40	60	79	99
68	2.4751	2.4876	2.5002	2.5129	2.5257	2.5386	2.5517	2.5649	2.5782	2.5916	22	43	65	87	108
69	2.6051	2.6187	2.6325	2.6464	2.6605	2.6746	2.6889	2.7034	2.7179	2.7326	24	47	71	95	119
70	2.7475	2.7625	2.7776	2.7929	2.8083	2.8239	2.8397	2.8556	2.8716	2.8878	26	52	78	104	131
71	2.9042	2.9208	2.9375	2.9544	2.9714	2.9887	3.0061	3.0237	3.0415	3.0595	29	58	87	116	145
72	3.0777	3.0961	3.1146	3.1334	3.1524	3.1716	3.1910	3.2106	3.2305	3.2506	32	64	96	129	161
73	3.2709	3.2914	3.3122	3.3332	3.3544	3.3759	3.3977	3.4197	3.4420	3.4646	36	72	108	144	180
74	3.4874	3.5105	3.5339	3.5576	3.5816	3.6059	3.6305	3.6554	3.6806	3.7062	41	81	122	163	204
75	3.7321	3.7583	3.7848	3.8118	3.8391	3.8667	3.8947	3.9232	3.9520	3.9812	46	93	139	186	232
76	4.0108	4.0408	4.0713	4.1022	4.1335	4.1653	4.1976	4.2303	4.2635	4.2972	53	107	160	213	267
77	4.3315	4.3662	4.4015	4.4374	4.4737	4.5107	4.5483	4.5864	4.6252	4.6646					
78	4.7046	4.7453	4.7867	4.8288	4.8716	4.9152	4.9594	5.0045	5.0504	5.0970					
79	5.1446	5.1929	5.2422	5.2924	5.3435	5.3955	5.4486	5.5026	5.5578	5.6140					
80	5.6713	5.7297	5.7894	5.8502	5.9124	5.9758	6.0405	6.1066	6.1742	6.2432	Differences				
81	6.3138	6.3859	6.4596	6.5350	6.6122	6.6912	6.7720	6.8548	6.9395	7.0264	untrustworthy				
82	7.1154	7.2066	7.3002	6.3962	7.4947	7.5958	7.6996	7.8062	7.9158	8.0285	here				
83	8.1443	8.2636	8.3863	8.5126	8.6427	8.7769	8.9152	9.0579	9.2052	9.3572					
84	9.5144	9.677	9.845	10.02	10.20	10.39	10.58	10.78	10.99	11.20					
85	11.43	11.66	11.91	12.16	12.43	12.71	13.00	13.30	13.62	13.95					
86	14.30	14.67	15.06	15.46	15.89	16.35	16.83	17.34	17.89	18.46					
87	19.08	19.74	20.45	21.20	22.02	22.90	23.86	24.90	26.03	27.27					
88	28.64	30.14	31.82	33.69	35.80	38.19	40.92	44.07	47.74	52.08					
89	57.29	63.66	71.62	81.85	95.49	114.6	143.2	191.0	286.5	573.0					
90	∞														

Quadrant	Angle	tan A =	Examples
first	0 to 90°	tan A	tan 56° 17' = 1.4986
second	90° to 180°	−tan (180° − A)	tan 123° 43' = −tan (180° − 123° 43')
third	180° to 270°	tan (A − 180°)	= −tan 56° 17' = −1.4986
fourth	270° to 360°	−tan (360° − A)	tan 236° 17' = tan (236° 17' − 180°)
			= tan 56° 17' = 1.4986
			tan 303° 43' = −tan (360° − 303° 43')
			= −tan 56° 17' = −1.4986

DEGREES TO RADIANS

°	0' 0.0°	6' 0.1°	12' 0.2°	18' 0.3°	24' 0.4°	30' 0.5°	36' 0.6°	42' 0.7°	48' 0.8°	54' 0.9°	1'	2'	3'	4'	5'
0	0.0000	0.0017	0.0035	0.0052	0.0070	0.0087	0.0105	0.0122	0.0140	0.0157	3	6	9	12	15
1	0.0175	0.0192	0.0209	0.0227	0.0244	0.0262	0.0279	0.0297	0.0314	0.0332	3	6	9	12	15
2	0.0349	0.0367	0.0384	0.0401	0.0419	0.0436	0.0454	0.0471	0.0489	0.0506	3	6	9	12	15
3	0.0524	0.0541	0.0559	0.0576	0.0593	0.0611	0.0628	0.0646	0.0663	0.0681	3	6	9	12	15
4	0.0698	0.0716	0.0733	0.0750	0.0768	0.0785	0.0803	0.0820	0.0838	0.0855	3	6	9	12	15
5	0.0873	0.0890	0.0908	0.0925	0.0942	0.0960	0.0977	0.0995	0.1012	0.1030	3	6	9	12	15
6	0.1047	0.1065	0.1082	0.1100	0.1117	0.1134	0.1152	0.1169	0.1187	0.1204	3	6	9	12	15
7	0.1222	0.1239	0.1257	0.1274	0.1292	0.1309	0.1326	0.1344	0.1361	0.1379	3	6	9	12	15
8	0.1396	0.1414	0.1431	0.1449	0.1466	0.1484	0.1501	0.1518	0.1536	0.1553	3	6	9	12	15
9	0.1571	0.1588	0.1606	0.1623	0.1641	0.1658	0.1676	0.1693	0.1710	0.1728	3	6	9	12	15
10	0.1745	0.1763	0.1780	0.1798	0.1815	0.1833	0.1850	0.1868	0.1885	0.1902	3	6	9	12	15
11	0.1920	0.1937	0.1955	0.1972	0.1990	0.2007	0.2025	0.2042	0.2060	0.2077	3	6	9	12	15
12	0.2094	0.2112	0.2129	0.2147	0.2164	0.2182	0.2199	0.2217	0.2234	0.2251	3	6	9	12	15
13	0.2269	0.2286	0.2304	0.2321	0.2339	0.2356	0.2374	0.2391	0.2409	0.2426	3	6	9	12	15
14	0.2443	0.2461	0.2478	0.2496	0.2513	0.2531	0.2548	0.2566	0.2583	0.2601	3	6	9	12	15
15	0.2618	0.2635	0.2653	0.2670	0.2688	0.2705	0.2723	0.2740	0.2758	0.2775	3	6	9	12	15
16	0.2793	0.2810	0.2827	0.2845	0.2862	0.2880	0.2897	0.2915	0.2932	0.2950	3	6	9	12	15
17	0.2967	0.2985	0.3002	0.3019	0.3037	0.3054	0.3072	0.3089	0.3107	0.3124	3	6	9	12	15
18	0.3142	0.3159	0.3176	0.3194	0.3211	0.3229	0.3246	0.3264	0.3281	0.3299	3	6	9	12	15
19	0.3316	0.3334	0.3351	0.3368	0.3386	0.3403	0.3421	0.3438	0.3456	0.3473	3	6	9	12	15
20	0.3491	0.3508	0.3526	0.3543	0.3560	0.3578	0.3595	0.3613	0.3630	0.3648	3	6	9	12	15
21	0.3665	0.3683	0.3700	0.3718	0.3735	0.3752	0.3770	0.3787	0.3805	0.3822	3	6	9	12	15
22	0.3840	0.3857	0.3875	0.3892	0.3910	0.3927	0.3944	0.3962	0.3979	0.3997	3	6	9	12	15
23	0.4014	0.4032	0.4049	0.4067	0.4084	0.4102	0.4119	0.4136	0.4154	0.4171	3	6	9	12	15
24	0.4189	0.4206	0.4224	0.4241	0.4259	0.4276	0.4294	0.4311	0.4328	0.4346	3	6	9	12	15
25	0.4363	0.4381	0.4398	0.4416	0.4433	0.4451	0.4468	0.4485	0.4503	0.4520	3	6	9	12	15
26	0.4538	0.4555	0.4573	0.4590	0.4608	0.4625	0.4643	0.4660	0.4677	0.4695	3	6	9	12	15
27	0.4712	0.4730	0.4747	0.4765	0.4782	0.4800	0.4817	0.4835	0.4852	0.4869	3	6	9	12	15
28	0.4887	0.4904	0.4922	0.4939	0.4957	0.4974	0.4992	0.5009	0.5027	0.5044	3	6	9	12	15
29	0.5061	0.5079	0.5096	0.5114	0.5131	0.5149	0.5166	0.5184	0.5201	0.5219	3	6	9	12	15
30	0.5236	0.5253	0.5271	0.5288	0.5306	0.5323	0.5341	0.5358	0.5376	0.5393	3	6	9	12	15
31	0.5411	0.5428	0.5445	0.5463	0.5480	0.5498	0.5515	0.5533	0.5550	0.5568	3	6	9	12	15
32	0.5585	0.5603	0.5620	0.5637	0.5655	0.5672	0.5690	0.5707	0.5725	0.5742	3	6	9	12	15
33	0.5760	0.5777	0.5794	0.5812	0.5829	0.5847	0.5864	0.5882	0.5899	0.5917	3	6	9	12	15
34	0.5934	0.5952	0.5969	0.5986	0.6004	0.6021	0.6039	0.6056	0.6074	0.6091	3	6	9	12	15
35	0.6109	0.6126	0.6144	0.6161	0.6178	0.6196	0.6213	0.6231	0.6248	0.6266	3	6	9	12	15
36	0.6283	0.6301	0.6318	0.6336	0.6353	0.6370	0.6388	0.6405	0.6423	0.6440	3	6	9	12	15
37	0.6458	0.6475	0.6493	0.6510	0.6528	0.6545	0.6562	0.6580	0.6597	0.6615	3	6	9	12	15
38	0.6632	0.6650	0.6667	0.6685	0.6702	0.6720	0.6737	0.6754	0.6772	0.6789	3	6	9	12	15
39	0.6807	0.6824	0.6842	0.6859	0.6877	0.6894	0.6912	0.6929	0.6946	0.6964	3	6	9	12	15
40	0.6981	0.6999	0.7016	0.7034	0.7051	0.7069	0.7086	0.7103	0.7121	0.7138	3	6	9	12	15
41	0.7156	0.7173	0.7191	0.7208	0.7226	0.7243	0.7261	0.7278	0.7295	0.7313	3	6	9	12	15
42	0.7330	0.7348	0.7365	0.7383	0.7400	0.7418	0.7435	0.7453	0.7470	0.7487	3	6	9	12	15
43	0.7505	0.7522	0.7540	0.7557	0.7575	0.7592	0.7610	0.7627	0.7645	0.7662	3	6	9	12	15
44	0.7679	0.7697	0.7714	0.7732	0.7749	0.7767	0.7784	0.7802	0.7819	0.7837	3	6	9	12	15
45	0.7854	0.7871	0.7889	0.7906	0.7924	0.7941	0.7959	0.7976	0.7994	0.8011	3	6	9	12	15

$$\theta° = \frac{\pi \times \theta°}{180} = 0.017\,45 \times \theta \text{ radians}$$

$$30° = \frac{\pi}{6} \text{ radians} \qquad 60° = \frac{\pi}{3} \text{ radians}$$

$$45° = \frac{\pi}{4} \text{ radians} \qquad 90° = \frac{\pi}{2} \text{ radians}$$

DEGREES TO RADIANS

°	0' 0.0°	6' 0.1°	12' 0.2°	18' 0.3°	24' 0.4°	30' 0.5°	36' 0.6°	42' 0.7°	48' 0.8°	54' 0.9°	1'	2'	3'	4'	5'
45	0.7854	0.7871	0.7889	0.7906	0.7924	0.7941	0.7959	0.7976	0.7994	0.8011	3	6	9	12	15
46	0.8029	0.8046	0.8063	0.8081	0.8098	0.8116	0.8133	0.8151	0.8168	0.8186	3	6	9	12	15
47	0.8203	0.8221	0.8238	0.8255	0.8273	0.8290	0.8308	0.8325	0.8343	0.8360	3	6	9	12	15
48	0.8378	0.8395	0.8412	0.8430	0.8447	0.8465	0.8482	0.8500	0.8517	0.8535	3	6	9	12	15
49	0.8552	0.8570	0.8587	0.8604	0.8622	0.8639	0.8657	0.8674	0.8692	0.8709	3	6	9	12	15
50	0.8727	0.8744	0.8762	0.8779	0.8796	0.8814	0.8831	0.8849	0.8866	0.8884	3	6	9	12	15
51	0.8901	0.8919	0.8936	0.8954	0.8971	0.8988	0.9006	0.9023	0.9041	0.9058	3	6	9	12	15
52	0.9076	0.9093	0.9111	0.9128	0.9146	0.9163	0.9180	0.9198	0.9215	0.9233	3	6	9	12	15
53	0.9250	0.9268	0.9285	0.9303	0.9320	0.9338	0.9355	0.9372	0.9390	0.9407	3	6	9	12	15
54	0.9425	0.9442	0.9460	0.9477	0.9495	0.9512	0.9529	0.9547	0.9564	0.9582	3	6	9	12	15
55	0.9599	0.9617	0.9634	0.9652	0.9669	0.9687	0.9704	0.9721	0.9739	0.9756	3	6	9	12	15
56	0.9774	0.9791	0.9809	0.9826	0.9844	0.9861	0.9879	0.9896	0.9913	0.9931	3	6	9	12	15
57	0.9948	0.9966	0.9983	1.0001	1.0018	1.0036	1.0053	1.0071	1.0088	1.0105	3	6	9	12	15
58	1.0123	1.0140	1.0158	1.0175	1.0193	1.0210	1.0228	1.0245	1.0263	1.0280	3	6	9	12	15
59	1.0297	1.0315	1.0332	1.0350	1.0367	1.0385	1.0402	1.0420	1.0437	1.0455	3	6	9	12	15
60	1.0472	1.0489	1.0507	1.0524	1.0542	1.0559	1.0577	1.0594	1.0612	1.0629	3	6	9	12	15
61	1.0647	1.0664	1.0681	1.0699	1.0716	1.0734	1.0751	1.0769	1.0786	1.0804	3	6	9	12	15
62	1.0821	1.0838	1.0856	1.0873	1.0891	1.0908	1.0926	1.0943	1.0961	1.0978	3	6	9	12	15
63	1.0996	1.1013	1.1030	1.1048	1.1065	1.1083	1.1100	1.1118	1.1135	1.1153	3	6	9	12	15
64	1.1170	1.1188	1.1205	1.1222	1.1240	1.1257	1.1275	1.1292	1.1310	1.1327	3	6	9	12	15
65	1.1345	1.1362	1.1380	1.1397	1.1414	1.1432	1.1449	1.1467	1.1484	1.1502	3	6	9	12	15
66	1.1519	1.1537	1.1554	1.1572	1.1589	1.1606	1.1624	1.1641	1.1659	1.1676	3	6	9	12	15
67	1.1694	1.1711	1.1729	1.1746	1.1764	1.1781	1.1798	1.1816	1.1833	1.1851	3	6	9	12	15
68	1.1868	1.1886	1.1903	1.1921	1.1938	1.1956	1.1973	1.1990	1.2008	1.2025	3	6	9	12	15
69	1.2043	1.2060	1.2078	1.2095	1.2113	1.2130	1.2147	1.2165	1.2182	1.2200	3	6	9	12	15
70	1.2217	1.2235	1.2252	1.2270	1.2287	1.2305	1.2322	1.2339	1.2357	1.2374	3	6	9	12	15
71	1.2392	1.2409	1.2427	1.2444	1.2462	1.2479	1.2497	1.2514	1.2531	1.2549	3	6	9	12	15
72	1.2566	1.2584	1.2601	1.2619	1.2636	1.2654	1.2671	1.2689	1.2706	1.2723	3	6	9	12	15
73	1.2741	1.2758	1.2776	1.2793	1.2811	1.2828	1.2846	1.2863	1.2881	1.2898	3	6	9	12	15
74	1.2915	1.2933	1.2950	1.2968	1.2985	1.3003	1.3020	1.3038	1.3055	1.3073	3	6	9	12	15
75	1.3090	1.3107	1.3125	1.3142	1.3160	1.3177	1.3195	1.3212	1.3230	1.3247	3	6	9	12	15
76	1.3265	1.3282	1.3299	1.3317	1.3334	1.3352	1.3369	1.3387	1.3404	1.3422	3	6	9	12	15
77	1.3439	1.3456	1.3474	1.3491	1.3509	1.3526	1.3544	1.3561	1.3579	1.3596	3	6	9	12	15
78	1.3614	1.3631	1.3648	1.3666	1.3683	1.3701	1.3718	1.3736	1.3753	1.3771	3	6	9	12	15
79	1.3788	1.3806	1.3823	1.3840	1.3858	1.3875	1.3893	1.3910	1.3928	1.3945	3	6	9	12	15
80	1.3963	1.3980	1.3998	1.4015	1.4032	1.4050	1.4067	1.4085	1.4102	1.4120	3	6	9	12	15
81	1.4137	1.4155	1.4172	1.4190	1.4207	1.4224	1.4242	1.4259	1.4277	1.4294	3	6	9	12	15
82	1.4312	1.4329	1.4347	1.4364	1.4382	1.4399	1.4416	1.4434	1.4451	1.4469	3	6	9	12	15
83	1.4486	1.4504	1.4521	1.4539	1.4556	1.4573	1.4591	1.4608	1.4626	1.4643	3	6	9	12	15
84	1.4661	1.4678	1.4696	1.4713	1.4731	1.4748	1.4765	1.4783	1.4800	1.4818	3	6	9	12	15
85	1.4835	1.4853	1.4870	1.4888	1.4905	1.4923	1.4940	1.4957	1.4975	1.4992	3	6	9	12	15
86	1.5010	1.5027	1.5045	1.5062	1.5080	1.5097	1.5115	1.5132	1.5149	1.5167	3	6	9	12	15
87	1.5184	1.5202	1.5219	1.5237	1.5254	1.5272	1.5289	1.5307	1.5324	1.5341	3	6	9	12	15
88	1.5359	1.5376	1.5394	1.5411	1.5429	1.5446	1.5464	1.5481	1.5499	1.5516	3	6	9	12	15
89	1.5533	1.5551	1.5568	1.5586	1.5603	1.5621	1.5638	1.5656	1.5673	1.5691	3	6	9	12	15

85° 46' = 1.4969 radians (direct from table)

0.6219 radians = 35° 38' (by finding 0.6219 in the table and reading off the corresponding angle in degrees).

NATURAL LOGARITHMS

	0	1	2	3	4	5	6	7	8	9	1	2	3	4	5	6	7	8	9
1.0	0.0000	0.0100	0.0198	0.0296	0.0392	0.0488	0.0583	0.0677	0.0770	0.0862	10	19	29	38	48	57	67	76	86
1.1	0.0953	0.1044	0.1133	0.1222	0.1310	0.1398	0.1484	0.1570	0.1655	0.1740	9	17	26	35	44	52	61	70	78
1.2	0.1823	0.1906	0.1989	0.2070	0.2151	0.2231	0.2311	0.2390	0.2469	0.2546	8	16	24	32	40	48	56	64	72
1.3	0.2624	0.2700	0.2776	0.2852	0.2927	0.3001	0.3075	0.3148	0.3221	0.3293	7	15	22	30	37	44	52	59	67
1.4	0.3365	0.3436	0.3507	0.3577	0.3646	0.3716	0.3784	0.3853	0.3920	0.3988	7	14	21	28	34	41	48	55	62
1.5	0.4055	0.4121	0.4187	0.4253	0.4318	0.4383	0.4447	0.4511	0.4574	0.4637	6	13	19	26	32	39	45	52	58
1.6	0.4700	0.4762	0.4824	0.4886	0.4947	0.5008	0.5068	0.5128	0.5188	0.5247	6	12	18	24	30	36	42	48	55
1.7	0.5306	0.5365	0.5423	0.5481	0.5539	0.5596	0.5653	0.5710	0.5766	0.5822	6	11	17	23	29	34	40	46	51
1.8	0.5878	0.5933	0.5988	0.6043	0.6098	0.6152	0.6206	0.6259	0.6313	0.6366	5	11	16	22	27	32	38	43	49
1.9	0.6419	0.6471	0.6523	0.6575	0.6627	0.6678	0.6729	0.6780	0.6831	0.6881	5	10	15	21	26	31	36	41	46
2.0	0.6931	0.6981	0.7031	0.7080	0.7129	0.7178	0.7227	0.7275	0.7324	0.7372	5	10	15	20	24	29	34	39	44
2.1	0.7419	0.7467	0.7514	0.7561	0.7608	0.7655	0.7701	0.7747	0.7793	0.7839	5	9	14	19	23	28	33	37	42
2.2	0.7885	0.7930	0.7975	0.8020	0.8065	0.8109	0.8154	0.8198	0.8242	0.8286	4	9	13	18	22	27	31	36	40
2.3	0.8329	0.8372	0.8416	0.8459	0.8502	0.8544	0.8587	0.8629	0.8671	0.8713	4	9	13	17	21	26	30	34	38
2.4	0.8755	0.8796	0.8838	0.8879	0.8920	0.8961	0.9002	0.9042	0.9083	0.9123	4	8	12	16	20	24	29	33	37
2.5	0.9163	0.9203	0.9243	0.9282	0.9322	0.9361	0.9400	0.9439	0.9478	0.9517	4	8	12	16	20	24	27	31	35
2.6	0.9555	0.9594	0.9632	0.9670	0.9708	0.9746	0.9783	0.9821	0.9858	0.9895	4	8	11	15	19	23	26	30	34
2.7	0.9933	0.9969	1.0006	1.0043	1.0080	1.0116	1.0152	1.0188	1.0225	1.0260	4	7	11	15	18	22	25	29	33
2.8	1.0296	1.0332	1.0367	1.0403	1.0438	1.0473	1.0508	1.0543	1.0578	1.0613	4	7	11	14	18	21	25	28	32
2.9	1.0647	1.0682	1.0716	1.0750	1.0784	1.0818	1.0852	1.0886	1.0919	1.0953	3	7	10	14	17	20	24	27	31
3.0	1.0986	1.1019	1.1053	1.1086	1.1119	1.1151	1.1184	1.1217	1.1249	1.1282	3	7	10	13	16	20	23	26	30
3.1	1.1314	1.1346	1.1378	1.1410	1.1442	1.1474	1.1506	1.1537	1.1569	1.1600	3	6	10	13	16	19	22	25	29
3.2	1.1632	1.1663	1.1694	1.1725	1.1756	1.1787	1.1817	1.1848	1.1878	1.1909	3	6	9	12	15	18	22	25	28
3.3	1.1939	1.1969	1.2000	1.2030	1.2060	1.2090	1.2119	1.2149	1.2179	1.2208	3	6	9	12	15	18	21	24	27
3.4	1.2238	1.2267	1.2296	1.2326	1.2355	1.2384	1.2413	1.2442	1.2470	1.2499	3	6	9	12	14	17	20	23	26
3.5	1.2528	1.2556	1.2585	1.2613	1.2641	1.2669	1.2698	1.2726	1.2754	1.2782	3	6	8	11	14	17	20	23	25
3.6	1.2809	1.2837	1.2865	1.2892	1.2920	1.2947	1.2975	1.3002	1.3029	1.3056	3	5	8	11	14	16	19	22	25
3.7	1.3083	1.3110	1.3137	1.3164	1.3191	1.3218	1.3244	1.3271	1.3297	1.3324	3	5	8	11	13	16	19	21	24
3.8	1.3350	1.3376	1.3403	1.3429	1.3455	1.3481	1.3507	1.3533	1.3558	1.3584	3	5	8	10	13	16	18	21	23
3.9	1.3610	1.3635	1.3661	1.3686	1.3712	1.3737	1.3762	1.3788	1.3813	1.3838	3	5	8	10	13	15	18	20	23
4.0	1.3863	1.3888	1.3913	1.3938	1.3962	1.3987	1.4012	1.4036	1.4061	1.4085	2	5	7	10	12	15	17	20	22
4.1	1.4110	1.4134	1.4159	1.4183	1.4207	1.4231	1.4255	1.4279	1.4303	1.4327	2	5	7	10	12	14	17	19	22
4.2	1.4351	1.4375	1.4398	1.4422	1.4446	1.4469	1.4493	1.4516	1.4540	1.4563	2	5	7	9	12	14	16	19	21
4.3	1.4586	1.4609	1.4633	1.4656	1.4679	1.4702	1.4725	1.4748	1.4770	1.4793	2	5	7	9	11	14	16	18	21
4.4	1.4816	1.4839	1.4861	1.4884	1.4907	1.4929	1.4951	1.4974	1.4996	1.5019	2	4	7	9	11	13	16	18	20
4.5	1.5041	1.5063	1.5085	1.5107	1.5129	1.5151	1.5173	1.5195	1.5217	1.5239	2	4	7	9	11	13	15	18	20
4.6	1.5261	1.5282	1.5304	1.5326	1.5347	1.5369	1.5390	1.5412	1.5433	1.5454	2	4	6	9	11	13	15	17	19
4.7	1.5476	1.5497	1.5518	1.5539	1.5560	1.5581	1.5602	1.5623	1.5644	1.5665	2	4	6	8	11	13	15	17	19
4.8	1.5686	1.5707	1.5728	1.5748	1.5769	1.5790	1.5810	1.5831	1.5851	1.5877	2	4	6	8	10	12	14	16	19
4.9	1.5892	1.5913	1.5933	1.5953	1.5974	1.5994	1.6014	1.6034	1.6054	1.6074	2	4	6	8	10	12	14	16	18
5.0	1.6094	1.6114	1.6134	1.6154	1.6174	1.6194	1.6214	1.6233	1.6253	1.6273	2	4	6	8	10	12	14	16	18
5.1	1.6292	1.6312	1.6332	1.6351	1.6371	1.6390	1.6409	1.6429	1.6448	1.6467	2	4	6	8	10	12	14	16	17
5.2	1.6487	1.6506	1.6525	1.6544	1.6563	1.6582	1.6601	1.6620	1.6639	1.6658	2	4	6	8	10	11	13	15	17
5.3	1.6677	1.6696	1.6715	1.6734	1.6752	1.6771	1.6790	1.6808	1.6827	1.6845	2	4	6	7	9	11	13	15	17
5.4	1.6864	1.6882	1.6901	1.6919	1.6938	1.6956	1.6974	1.6993	1.7011	1.7029	2	4	6	7	9	11	13	15	17

Natural logarithms of 10^{+n}

n	1	2	3	4	5	6	7	8	9
$\ln 10^{+n}$	2.3026	4.6052	6.9078	9.2103	11.5129	13.8155	16.1181	18.4207	20.7233

To find $\log_e 483.4$

$$483.4 = 4.834 \times 100 = 4.834 \times 10^2$$

$$\log_e 483.4 = \log_e 4.834 + \log_e 10^2$$

$$= 1.5756 + 4.6052 = 6.1808$$

NATURAL LOGARITHMS

	0	1	2	3	4	5	6	7	8	9	1 2 3	4 5 6	7 8 9
5.5	1.7047	1.7066	1.7084	1.7102	1.7120	1.7138	1.7156	1.7174	1.7192	1.7210	2 4 5	7 9 11	13 14 16
5.6	1.7228	1.7246	1.7263	1.7281	1.7299	1.7317	1.7334	1.7352	1.7370	1.7387	2 4 5	7 9 11	12 14 16
5.7	1.7405	1.7422	1.7440	1.7457	1.7475	1.7492	1.7509	1.7527	1.7544	1.7561	2 3 5	7 9 10	12 14 16
5.8	1.7579	1.7596	1.7613	1.7630	1.7647	1.7664	1.7681	1.7699	1.7716	1.7733	2 3 5	7 9 10	12 14 15
5.9	1.7750	1.7766	1.7783	1.7800	1.7817	1.7834	1.7851	1.7867	1.7884	1.7901	2 3 5	7 8 10	12 13 15
6.0	1.7918	1.7934	1.7951	1.7967	1.7984	1.8001	1.8017	1.8034	1.8050	1.8066	2 3 5	7 8 10	12 13 15
6.1	1.8083	1.8099	1.8116	1.8132	1.8148	1.8165	1.8181	1.8197	1.8213	1.8229	2 3 5	7 8 10	11 13 15
6.2	1.8245	1.8262	1.8278	1.8294	1.8310	1.8326	1.8342	1.8358	1.8374	1.8390	2 3 5	6 8 10	11 13 14
6.3	1.8405	1.8421	1.8437	1.8453	1.8469	1.8485	1.8500	1.8516	1.8532	1.8547	2 3 5	6 8 9	11 13 14
6.4	1.8563	1.8579	1.8594	1.8610	1.8625	1.8641	1.8656	1.8672	1.8687	1.8703	2 3 5	6 8 9	11 12 14
6.5	1.8718	1.8733	1.8749	1.8764	1.8779	1.8795	1.8810	1.8825	1.8840	1.8856	2 3 5	6 8 9	11 12 14
6.6	1.8871	1.8886	1.8901	1.8916	1.8931	1.8946	1.8961	1.8976	1.8991	1.9006	2 3 5	6 8 9	11 12 14
6.7	1.9021	1.9036	1.9051	1.9066	1.9081	1.9095	1.9110	1.9125	1.9140	1.9155	1 3 4	6 7 9	10 12 13
6.8	1.9169	1.9184	1.9199	1.9213	1.9228	1.9242	1.9257	1.9272	1.9286	1.9301	1 3 4	6 7 9	10 12 13
6.9	1.9315	1.9330	1.9344	1.9359	1.9373	1.9387	1.9402	1.9416	1.9430	1.9445	1 3 4	6 7 9	10 12 13
7.0	1.9459	1.9473	1.9488	1.9502	1.9516	1.9530	1.9544	1.9559	1.9573	1.9587	1 3 4	6 7 9	10 11 13
7.1	1.9601	1.9615	1.9629	1.9643	1.9657	1.9671	1.9685	1.9699	1.9713	1.9727	1 3 4	6 7 8	10 11 13
7.2	1.9741	1.9755	1.9769	1.9782	1.9796	1.9810	1.9824	1.9838	1.9851	1.9865	1 3 4	6 7 8	10 11 12
7.3	1.9879	1.9892	1.9906	1.9920	1.9933	1.9947	1.9961	1.9974	1.9988	2.0001	1 3 4	5 7 8	10 11 12
7.4	2.0015	2.0028	2.0042	2.0055	2.0069	2.0082	2.0096	2.0109	2.0122	2.0136	1 3 4	5 7 8	9 11 12
7.5	2.0149	2.0162	2.0176	2.0189	2.0202	2.0215	2.0229	2.0242	2.0255	2.0268	1 3 4	5 7 8	9 11 12
7.6	2.0281	2.0295	2.0308	2.0321	2.0334	2.0347	2.0360	2.0373	2.0386	2.0399	1 3 4	5 7 8	9 10 12
7.7	2.0412	2.0425	2.0438	2.0451	2.0464	2.0477	2.0490	2.0503	2.0516	2.0528	1 3 4	5 6 8	9 10 12
7.8	2.0541	2.0554	2.0567	2.0580	2.0592	2.0605	2.0618	2.0631	2.0643	2.0656	1 3 4	5 6 8	9 10 11
7.9	2.0669	2.0681	2.0694	2.0707	2.0719	2.0732	2.0744	2.0757	2.0769	2.0782	1 3 4	5 6 8	9 10 11
8.0	2.0794	2.0807	2.0819	2.0832	2.0844	2.0857	2.0869	2.0882	2.0894	2.0906	1 2 4	5 6 7	9 10 11
8.1	2.0919	2.0931	2.0943	2.0956	2.0968	2.0980	2.0992	2.1005	2.1017	2.1029	1 2 4	5 6 7	9 10 11
8.2	2.1041	2.1054	2.1066	2.1078	2.1090	2.1102	2.1114	2.1126	2.1138	2.1150	1 2 4	5 6 7	8 10 11
8.3	2.1163	2.1175	2.1187	2.1199	2.1211	2.1223	2.1235	2.1247	2.1258	2.1270	1 2 4	5 6 7	8 10 11
8.4	2.1282	2.1294	2.1306	2.1318	2.1330	2.1342	2.1353	2.1365	2.1377	2.1389	1 2 4	5 6 7	8 9 11
8.5	2.1401	2.1412	2.1424	2.1436	2.1448	2.1459	2.1471	2.1483	2.1494	2.1506	1 2 4	5 6 7	8 9 11
8.6	2.1518	2.1529	2.1541	2.1552	2.1564	2.1576	2.1587	2.1599	2.1610	2.1622	1 2 3	5 6 7	8 9 10
8.7	2.1633	2.1645	2.1656	2.1668	2.1679	2.1691	2.1702	2.1713	2.1725	2.1736	1 2 3	5 6 7	8 9 10
8.8	2.1748	2.1759	2.1770	2.1782	2.1793	2.1804	2.1815	2.1827	2.1838	2.1849	1 2 3	5 6 7	8 9 10
8.9	2.1861	2.1872	2.1883	2.1894	2.1905	2.1917	2.1928	2.1939	2.1950	2.1961	1 2 3	4 6 7	8 9 10
9.0	2.1972	2.1983	2.1994	2.2006	2.2017	2.2028	2.2039	2.2050	2.2061	2.2072	1 2 3	4 6 7	8 9 10
9.1	2.2083	2.2094	2.2105	2.2116	2.2127	2.2138	2.2148	2.2159	2.2170	2.2181	1 2 3	4 5 7	8 9 10
9.2	2.2192	2.2203	2.2214	2.2225	2.2235	2.2246	2.2257	2.2268	2.2279	2.2289	1 2 3	4 5 6	8 9 10
9.3	2.2300	2.2311	2.2322	2.2332	2.2343	2.2354	2.2364	2.2375	2.2386	2.2396	1 2 3	4 5 6	7 9 10
9.4	2.2407	2.2418	2.2428	2.2439	2.2450	2.2460	2.2471	2.2481	2.2492	2.2502	1 2 3	4 5 6	7 8 10
9.5	2.2513	2.2523	2.2534	2.2544	2.2555	2.2565	2.2576	2.2586	2.2597	2.2607	1 2 3	4 5 6	7 8 9
9.6	2.2618	2.2628	2.2638	2.2649	2.2659	2.2670	2.2680	2.2690	2.2701	2.2711	1 2 3	4 5 6	7 8 9
9.7	2.2721	2.2732	2.2742	2.2752	2.2762	2.2773	2.2783	2.2793	2.2803	2.2814	1 2 3	4 5 6	7 8 9
9.8	2.2824	2.2834	2.2844	2.2854	2.2865	2.2875	2.2885	2.2895	2.2905	2.2915	1 2 3	4 5 6	7 8 9
9.9	2.2925	2.2935	2.2946	2.2956	2.2966	2.2976	2.2986	2.2996	2.3006	2.3016	1 2 3	4 5 6	7 8 9

Natural logarithms of 10^{-n}

n	1	2	3	4	5	6	7	8	9
$\ln 10^{-n}$	$\bar{3}.6974$	$\bar{5}.3948$	$\bar{7}.0922$	$\overline{10}.7897$	$\overline{12}.4871$	$\overline{14}.1845$	$\overline{17}.8819$	$\overline{19}.5793$	$\overline{21}.2767$

To find $\log_e 0.053\,61$

$$0.053\,61 = \frac{5.361}{100} = \frac{5.361}{10^2} = 5.361 \times 10^{-2}$$

$$\log_e 0.053\,61 = \log_e 5.361 + \log_e 10^{-2}$$
$$= 1.6792 + \bar{5}.3948 = \bar{3}.0740$$
$$= -3 + 0.0740 = -2.9260$$

41

TABLE OF e^x

x	.00	.01	.02	.03	.04	.05	.06	.07	.08	.09
0.0	1.0000	1.0101	1.0202	1.0305	1.0408	1.0513	1.0618	1.0725	1.0833	1.0942
0.1	1.1052	1.1163	1.1275	1.1388	1.1503	1.1618	1.1735	1.1853	1.1972	1.2092
0.2	1.2214	1.2337	1.2461	1.2586	1.2712	1.2840	1.2969	1.3100	1.3231	1.3364
0.3	1.3499	1.3634	1.3771	1.3910	1.4049	1.4191	1.4333	1.4477	1.4623	1.4770
0.4	1.4918	1.5068	1.5220	1.5373	1.5527	1.5683	1.5841	1.6000	1.6161	1.6323
0.5	1.6487	1.6653	1.6820	1.6989	1.7160	1.7333	1.7507	1.7683	1.7860	1.8040
0.6	1.8221	1.8404	1.8589	1.8776	1.8965	1.9155	1.9348	1.9542	1.9739	1.9937
0.7	2.0138	2.0340	2.0544	2.0751	2.0959	2.1170	2.1383	2.1598	2.1815	2.2034
0.8	2.2255	2.2479	2.2705	2.2933	2.3164	2.3396	2.3632	2.3869	2.4109	2.4351
0.9	2.4596	2.4843	2.5093	2.5345	2.5600	2.5857	2.6117	2.6379	2.6645	2.6912
1.0	2.7183	2.7456	2.7732	2.8011	2.8292	2.8576	2.8864	2.9154	2.9447	2.9743
1.1	3.0042	3.0344	3.0649	3.0957	3.1268	3.1582	3.1899	3.2220	3.2544	3.2871
1.2	3.3201	3.3535	3.3872	3.4212	3.4556	3.4903	3.5254	3.5608	3.5966	3.6328
1.3	3.6693	3.7062	3.7434	3.7810	3.8190	3.8574	3.8962	3.9354	3.9749	4.0149
1.4	4.0552	4.0960	4.1371	4.1787	4.2207	4.2631	4.3060	4.3492	4.3929	4.4371
1.5	4.4817	4.5267	4.5722	4.6182	4.6646	4.7115	4.7588	4.8066	4.8550	4.9037
1.6	4.9530	5.0028	5.0531	5.1039	5.1552	5.2070	5.2593	5.3122	5.3656	5.4195
1.7	5.4739	5.5290	5.5845	5.6407	5.6973	5.7546	5.8124	5.8709	5.9299	5.9895
1.8	6.0496	6.1104	6.1719	6.2339	6.2965	6.3598	6.4237	6.4883	6.5535	6.6194
1.9	6.6859	6.7531	6.8210	6.8895	6.9588	7.0287	7.0993	7.1707	7.2427	7.3155
2.0	7.3891	7.4633	7.5383	7.6141	7.6906	7.7679	7.8460	7.9248	8.0045	8.0849
2.1	8.1662	8.2482	8.3311	8.4149	8.4994	8.5849	8.6711	8.7583	8.8463	8.9352
2.2	9.0250	9.1157	9.2073	9.2999	9.3933	9.4877	9.5831	9.6794	9.7767	9.8749
2.3	9.9742	10.074	10.176	10.278	10.381	10.486	10.591	10.697	10.805	10.913
2.4	11.023	11.134	11.246	11.359	11.473	11.588	11.705	11.822	11.941	12.061
2.5	12.183	12.305	12.429	12.554	12.680	12.807	12.936	13.066	13.197	13.330
2.6	13.464	13.599	13.736	13.874	14.013	14.154	14.296	14.440	14.585	14.732
2.7	14.880	15.029	15.180	15.333	15.487	15.643	15.800	15.959	16.119	16.281
2.8	16.445	16.610	16.777	16.945	17.116	17.288	17.462	17.637	17.814	17.993
2.9	18.174	18.357	18.541	18.728	18.916	19.106	19.298	19.492	19.688	19.886
3.0	20.086	20.287	20.491	20.697	20.905	21.115	21.327	21.542	21.758	21.977
3.1	22.198	22.421	22.646	22.874	23.104	23.336	23.571	23.808	24.047	24.288
3.2	24.533	24.779	25.028	25.280	25.534	25.790	26.050	26.311	26.576	26.843
3.3	27.113	27.385	27.660	27.938	28.219	28.503	28.789	29.079	29.371	29.666
3.4	29.964	30.265	30.569	30.877	31.187	31.500	31.817	32.137	32.460	32.786
3.5	33.115	33.448	33.784	34.124	34.467	34.813	35.163	35.517	35.874	36.234
3.6	36.598	36.966	37.338	37.713	38.092	38.475	38.861	39.252	39.646	40.045
3.7	40.447	40.854	41.264	41.679	42.098	42.521	42.948	43.380	43.816	44.256
3.8	44.701	45.150	45.604	46.063	46.525	46.993	47.465	47.942	48.424	48.911
3.9	49.402	49.899	50.400	50.907	51.419	51.935	52.457	52.985	53.517	54.055
4.0	54.598									

x	e^x	x	e^x	x	e^x	x	e^x	x	e^x	x	e^x
4.1	60.340	4.6	99.484	5.1	164.02	5.6	270.43	6.1	445.86	6.6	735.10
4.2	66.686	4.7	109.95	5.2	181.27	5.7	298.87	6.2	492.75	6.7	812.41
4.3	73.700	4.8	121.51	5.3	200.34	5.8	330.30	6.3	544.57	6.8	897.85
4.4	81.451	4.9	134.29	5.4	221.41	5.9	365.04	6.4	601.85	6.9	992.27
4.5	90.017	5.0	148.41	5.5	244.69	6.0	403.43	6.5	665.14	7.0	1096.63

TABLE OF e^{-x}

x	.00	.01	.02	.03	.04	.05	.06	.07	.08	.09
0.0	1.0000	0.9900	0.9802	0.9704	0.9608	0.9512	0.9418	0.9324	0.9231	0.9139
0.1	0.9048	0.8958	0.8869	0.8781	0.8694	0.8607	0.8521	0.8437	0.8353	0.8270
0.2	0.8187	0.8106	0.8025	0.7945	0.7866	0.7788	0.7711	0.7634	0.7558	0.7483
0.3	0.7408	0.7334	0.7261	0.7189	0.7118	0.7047	0.6977	0.6907	0.6839	0.6771
0.4	0.6703	0.6637	0.6570	0.6505	0.6440	0.6376	0.6313	0.6250	0.6188	0.6126
0.5	0.6065	0.6005	0.5945	0.5886	0.5827	0.5769	0.5712	0.5655	0.5599	0.5543
0.6	0.5488	0.5434	0.5379	0.5326	0.5273	0.5220	0.5169	0.5117	0.5066	0.5016
0.7	0.4966	0.4916	0.4868	0.4819	0.4771	0.4724	0.4677	0.4630	0.4584	0.4538
0.8	0.4493	0.4449	0.4404	0.4360	0.4317	0.4274	0.4232	0.4190	0.4148	0.4107
0.9	0.4066	0.4025	0.3985	0.3946	0.3906	0.3867	0.3829	0.3791	0.3753	0.3716
1.0	0.3679	0.3642	0.3606	0.3570	0.3535	0.3499	0.3465	0.3430	0.3396	0.3362
1.1	0.3329	0.3296	0.3263	0.3230	0.3198	0.3166	0.3135	0.3104	0.3073	0.3042
1.2	0.3012	0.2982	0.2952	0.2923	0.2894	0.2865	0.2837	0.2808	0.2780	0.2753
1.3	0.2725	0.2698	0.2671	0.2645	0.2618	0.2592	0.2567	0.2541	0.2516	0.2491
1.4	0.2466	0.2441	0.2417	0.2393	0.2369	0.2346	0.2322	0.2299	0.2276	0.2254
1.5	0.2231	0.2209	0.2187	0.2165	0.2144	0.2122	0.2101	0.2080	0.2060	0.2039
1.6	0.2019	0.1999	0.1979	0.1959	0.1940	0.1920	0.1901	0.1882	0.1864	0.1845
1.7	0.1827	0.1809	0.1791	0.1773	0.1755	0.1738	0.1720	0.1703	0.1686	0.1670
1.8	0.1653	0.1637	0.1620	0.1604	0.1588	0.1572	0.1557	0.1541	0.1526	0.1511
1.9	0.1496	0.1481	0.1466	0.1451	0.1437	0.1423	0.1409	0.1395	0.1381	0.1367
2.0	0.1353	0.1340	0.1327	0.1313	0.1300	0.1287	0.1275	0.1262	0.1249	0.1237
2.1	0.1225	0.1212	0.1200	0.1188	0.1177	0.1165	0.1153	0.1142	0.1130	0.1119
2.2	0.1108	0.1097	0.1086	0.1075	0.1065	0.1054	0.1044	0.1033	0.1023	0.1013
2.3	0.1003	0.0993	0.0983	0.0973	0.0963	0.0954	0.0944	0.0935	0.0925	0.0916
2.4	0.0907	0.0898	0.0889	0.0880	0.0872	0.0863	0.0854	0.0846	0.0837	0.0829
2.5	0.0821	0.0813	0.0805	0.0797	0.0789	0.0781	0.0773	0.0765	0.0758	0.0750
2.6	0.0743	0.0735	0.0728	0.0721	0.0714	0.0707	0.0699	0.0693	0.0686	0.0679
2.7	0.0672	0.0665	0.0659	0.0652	0.0646	0.0639	0.0633	0.0627	0.0620	0.0614
2.8	0.0608	0.0602	0.0596	0.0590	0.0584	0.0578	0.0573	0.0567	0.0561	0.0556
2.9	0.0550	0.0545	0.0539	0.0534	0.0529	0.0523	0.0518	0.0513	0.0508	0.0503
3.0	0.0498	0.0493	0.0488	0.0483	0.0478	0.0474	0.0469	0.0464	0.0460	0.0455
3.1	0.0450	0.0446	0.0442	0.0437	0.0433	0.0429	0.0424	0.0420	0.0416	0.0412
3.2	0.0408	0.0404	0.0400	0.0396	0.0392	0.0388	0.0384	0.0380	0.0376	0.0373
3.3	0.0369	0.0365	0.0362	0.0358	0.0354	0.0351	0.0347	0.0344	0.0340	0.0337
3.4	0.0334	0.0330	0.0327	0.0324	0.0321	0.0317	0.0314	0.0311	0.0308	0.0305
3.5	0.0302	0.0299	0.0296	0.0293	0.0290	0.0287	0.0284	0.0282	0.0279	0.0276
3.6	0.0273	0.0271	0.0268	0.0265	0.0263	0.0260	0.0257	0.0255	0.0252	0.0250
3.7	0.0247	0.0245	0.0242	0.0240	0.0238	0.0235	0.0233	0.0231	0.0228	0.0226
3.8	0.0224	0.0221	0.0219	0.0217	0.0215	0.0213	0.0211	0.0209	0.0207	0.0204
3.9	0.0202	0.0200	0.0198	0.0196	0.0194	0.0193	0.0191	0.0189	0.0187	0.0185
4.0	0.0183									

e^{-x} for values of x greater than 4.0 may be found by using the table of natural logarithms and a reciprocal table (or calculator).

To find $e^{-4.5361}$

If $y = e^{4.5361}$ then from the e^x table y is about 90.

Since 4.5361 is outside the range of values given in the natural logarithm tables, we use the table of natural logarithms of 10^{+n}

We find that $\log_e 10 = 2.3026$

and hence $\log_e y = 2.3026 + 2.2335$

$\log_e 9.333 = 2.2335$ (using the natural logarithm table)

Hence $e^{4.5361} = 9.333 \times 10 = 93.33$

$e^{-4.5361} = 0.010\ 72$ (using a table of reciprocals)

43

COMPLEX NUMBERS

If x and y are real numbers and $i = \sqrt{-1}$ then the complex number $z = x + iy$ consists of the real part x and the imaginary part iy.

$\bar{z} = x - iy$ is the conjugate of the complex number $z = x + iy$.

If $x + iy = a + ib$ then $x = a$ and $y = b$

$$(a + ib) + (c + id) = (a + c) + i(b + d)$$

$$(a + ib) - (c + id) = (a - c) + i(b - d)$$

$$(a + ib)(c + id) = (ac - bd) + i(ad + bc)$$

$$\frac{a + ib}{c + id} = \frac{ac + bd}{c^2 + d^2} + i\frac{bc - ad}{c^2 + d^2}$$

Every complex number may be written in polar form. Thus

$$x + iy = r(\cos\theta + i\sin\theta) = r\angle\theta$$

r is called the modulus of z and this may be written $r = |z|$

$$r = \sqrt{x^2 + y^2}$$

θ is called the argument and this may be written $\theta = \arg z$

$$\tan\theta = \frac{y}{x}$$

If $z_1 = r_1(\cos\theta_1 + i\sin\theta_1)$ and $z_2 = r_2(\cos\theta_2 + i\sin\theta_2)$

$$z_1 z_2 = r_1 r_2[\cos(\theta_1 + \theta_2) + i\sin(\theta_1 + \theta_2)] = r_1 r_2 \angle(\theta_1 + \theta_2)$$

$$\frac{z_1}{z_2} = \frac{r_1[\cos(\theta_1 - \theta_2) + i\sin(\theta_1 - \theta_2)]}{r_2} = \frac{r_1}{r_2}\angle(\theta_1 - \theta_2)$$

Exponential form

$$z = re^{i\theta}$$

De Moivre's theorem

$$(\cos\theta + i\sin\theta)^n = \cos n\theta + i\sin n\theta$$

where n is any real number

$$\sin\theta = \frac{e^{i\theta} - e^{-i\theta}}{2i}$$

$$\cos\theta = \frac{e^{i\theta} + e^{-i\theta}}{2}$$

$$\sin i\theta = i\sinh\theta \qquad \sinh i\theta = i\sin\theta$$

$$\cos i\theta = \cosh\theta \qquad \cosh i\theta = \cos\theta$$

CALCULATORS

Calculator check

Not all calculators have the same logic and the keys and stores do not always work in the same way. Before starting to perform strings of calculations check that you are using the calculator correctly. The following can be used to check the logic of the calculator.

$67.84 + 91.92 + 71.85 = 231.61$

$66.32 - 19.85 = 46.47$

$88.56 - 13.84 + 24.31 = 99.03$

$77.3 \times 64.8 = 5009.04$

$91.76 \times 3.84 + 817.52 = 1169.8784$

$(7.85 + 3.91) \times 83.64 = 983.6064$

$91.3 \times 43.2 \times 68.0 = 268\ 202.88$

$\dfrac{91.76}{1.85} = 49.6$

$\dfrac{81.32 \times 14.63}{76.51} = 15.549\ 753$

$\dfrac{84.3}{91.2} + \dfrac{76.51}{3.84} = 20.848\ 821$

For calculators without a memory this may be calculated thus:

$$\left(\dfrac{84.3 \times 3.84}{91.2} + 76.51\right) \div 3.84 = 20.848\ 821$$

$\dfrac{816.1}{94.3} - \dfrac{36.2}{14.7} = 6.191\ 709\ 8$

For calculators without a memory this may be calculated thus:

$$\left(\dfrac{-36.2 \times 94.3}{14.7} + 816.1\right) \div 94.3 = 6.191\ 709\ 8$$

$17.62 - \dfrac{8.54}{3.61} = 15.254\ 35$

Rounding off numbers

Significant figures (s.f.)

784 is a whole number.

784.6 is 785 when rounded off to the nearest whole number.

784.3 is 784 when rounded off to the nearest whole number.

In the number 784, the 7 is the most significant figure because it has the greatest value. The 8 is the next significant figure but 4 is the least significant figure because it has the smallest value.

The rules regarding significant figures are as follows:

(i) If the first figure to be discarded is 5 or more, increase the previous figure by 1.

> 981.7654 becomes 981.765 to six s.f.
> becomes 981.77 to five s.f.
> becomes 981.8 to four s.f.
> becomes 982 to three s.f.

(ii) Zeros must be kept to show the position of the decimal point or to indicate that zero is a significant figure.

> 78 652 becomes 78 650 to four s.f.
> becomes 78 700 to three s.f.
> becomes 79 000 to two s.f.
> becomes 80 000 to one s.f.

> 0.0849 becomes 0.085 to two s.f.
> becomes 0.09 to one s.f.

> 27.603 becomes 27.60 to four s.f.
> becomes 27.6 to three s.f.

Decimal places (d.p.)

The number 86.573 is said to have three decimal places because there are three figures to the right of the decimal point. The rules are similar to those used for significant figures.

(i) If the first figure to be discarded is 5 or more, increase the previous figure by 1.

> 5.865 becomes 5.87 to two d.p.
> becomes 5.9 to one d.p.

(ii) Zeros must be kept to show the size of the number or to indicate that zero is one of the decimal places.

> 0.008 362 becomes 0.008 36 to five d.p.
> becomes 0.0084 to four d.p.
> becomes 0.008 to three d.p.

> 7.603 becomes 7.60 to two d.p.
> becomes 7.6 to one d.p.

To find the square of a number

Enter the number and press the x^2 key.

Alternatively, enter the number and press the $\times$ and $=$ keys.

Example Find 87.92^2

Input	Display
87.92	87.92
x^2	7729.9264

Alternatively

Input	Display
87.92	87.92
×	87.92
=	7729.9264

To find the square root of a number

Enter the number and press $\sqrt{\ }$ key.

Example Find the square root of 785.62

Input	Display
785.62	785.62
$\sqrt{\ }$	28.02 ...

To find the reciprocal of a number

Enter the number and press the $\frac{1}{x}$ key.

Example Find the reciprocal of 0.8752

Input	Display
0.8752	0.8752
$\frac{1}{x}$	1.1425 ...

To find a number raised to the power *y*

Enter the number and press the x^y key, enter y and press = key.

Example Find 8.77^5

Input	Display
8.77	8.77
x^y	8.77
5	5.0
=	51879.76

47

To find the root of a number

Enter the number and press the x^y key. Now enter the number giving the power of the root to be found. Press the $\dfrac{1}{x}$ key and then the = key.

Example Find $\sqrt[3]{179.63}$
Note that $\sqrt[3]{179.63} = 179.63^{1/3}$

Input	Display
179.63	179.63
x^y	179.63
3	3.0
$\dfrac{1}{x}$	0.3333 ...
=	5.642 ...

To find e^x

Enter the value of x and press the e^x key.

Example Find $e^{1.754}$

Input	Display
1.754	1.754
e^x	5.777 ...

To find ln x

Enter the value of x and press the ln key. Note that ln x is often written $\log_e x$.

Example Find ln 91.87

Input	Display
91.87	91.87
ln	4.520 ...

Angles

Some calculators will accept angles stated in degrees, minutes and seconds but generally they will only accept angles stated in degrees and decimals of a degree or in radians.

Angles in degrees, minutes and seconds

There are 60 minutes in one degree.
There are 60 seconds in one minute.

An angle of 37 degrees, 21 minutes, 42 seconds is written 37° 21′ 42″.

Angles in decimal form

Angles stated in degrees and decimals of a degree are usually given correct to two decimal places.

For example, 48.76°.

To change from degrees, minutes and seconds to degrees in decimal form:
Divide the seconds by 60 and add on the minutes.
Divide the total minutes by 60 and add on the degrees.

Example Express 38° 27′ 56″ in decimals

$$\frac{56}{60} = 0.9333;\ 27 + 0.9333 = 27.9333$$

$$\frac{27.9333}{60} = 0.47;\ 38 + 0.47 = 38.47°$$

Using a calculator the method is:

Input	Display
56	56.0
÷	56.0
60	60.0
=	0.9333 . . .
+	0.9333 . . .
27	27.0
=	27.9333 . . .
÷	27.9333 . . .
60	60.0
=	0.4655 . . .
+	0.4655 . . .
38	38.0
=	38.4655

To change from degrees and decimals of a degree:
Take the decimal part and multiply by 60.
Take the decimal part of this product and multiply by 60.

Example Express 78.43° in degrees and minutes

$$0.43 \times 60 = 25.8′$$

$$0.8 \times 60 = 48″$$

$$78.43° = 78° 25′ 48″$$

Using a calculator the method is:

Input	Display	
0.43	0.43	
×	0.43	
60	60.0	
=	25.8	(record 25)
0.8	0.8	
×	0.8	
60	60.0	
=	48.0	(record 48)

Radians

Angles may be given in radians.
$180° = \pi$ radians, is used for conversions.

Degrees to radians multiply by $\dfrac{\pi}{180}$

Example Convert 87.43° to radians

$$87.43° = 87.43 \times \frac{\pi}{180} = 1.5259 \text{ radians}$$

Radians to degrees multiply by $\dfrac{180}{\pi}$

Example Convert 1.7623 radians to degrees

$$1.7623 \text{ rad} = 1.7623 \times \frac{180}{\pi} = 100.97°$$

In some cases calculations are made using radians. For example:

Area of sector of a circle $= \dfrac{1}{2} r^2 \theta$

Length of an arc of a circle $= r\theta$

where r is the radius and θ is the sector angle in radians (see below).

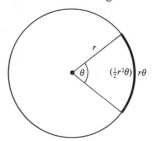

When doing calculations involving radians the calculator should be set to the radian mode.

When using a trigonometric series or calculus, the angle is in radians. For example,

$$\sin x = x - \frac{x^3}{3!} + \frac{x^5}{5!} - \ldots x \text{ in radians}$$

Example Find the value of $\displaystyle\int_0^{\pi/6} \sin 2x \, dx$

$$\int_0^{\pi/6} \sin 2x \, dx = \left[-\frac{1}{2} \cos 2x \right]_0^{\pi/6}$$

$$= -\frac{1}{2} \cos \frac{\pi}{3} + \frac{1}{2} \cos 0$$

$$= -0.25 + 0.5$$

$$= +0.25$$

Note that x is in radians

$$x = \frac{\pi}{6} \text{ radians (i.e., 30°).}$$

The sine of an angle

To obtain the sine of an angle enter the angle and press the sine key.

If the angle is in degrees, minutes and seconds first change it to the decimal form. Make sure that the calculator is set in the degree mode.

$$\sin 72.84° = 0.9555$$

$$\sin 289.61° = -0.9420$$

$$\sin 49° \ 18' \ 42'' = 49.31 = 0.7583$$

If the angle is given in radians make sure that the calculator is set in the radian mode.

$$\sin 2.8314 \text{ radians} = 0.3052$$

Usually a calculator will give only one value for θ for any given value of $\sin \theta$.

Thus $\qquad \sin \theta = 0.4732$ gives $\theta = 28.24°$

As shown below the sine curve is periodic with a period of 360°.

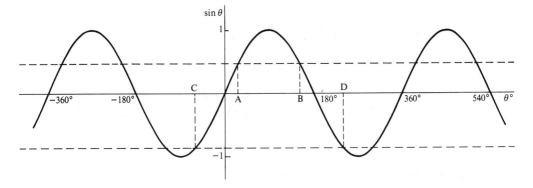

Hence when $\sin \theta = 0.4732$

$$\theta = 28.24° \text{ (A)} \pm 360n°$$

where n is zero or an integer

But also

$$\theta = (180° - 28.24°) \text{ (B)} \pm 360n°$$

Hence when $\sin \theta = 0.4732$

$$\theta = 28.24° \pm 360n° \text{ or } 151.76° \pm 360n°$$

Example When $\sin \theta = -0.8754$

$$\theta = -61.09° \text{ (C)} \pm 360n°$$

or $\qquad\qquad \theta = (180° + 61.09°) \text{ (D)} \pm 360n°$

Hence in all cases if the angle given by the calculator is $\alpha°$, then

$$\theta° = \alpha° \pm 360n°$$

or $\qquad\qquad \theta° = (180° - \alpha°) \pm 360n°$

The *cosecant* of an angle is the reciprocal of the sine of the angle. Thus

$$\text{cosec } \theta = \frac{1}{\sin \theta}$$

51

Example Find cosec 71.27°

$$\text{cosec } 71.27° = \frac{1}{\sin 71.27°} = 1.0559$$

Using a calculator the method is:

Input	Display
71.27	71.27
sin	0.9470 ...
$\dfrac{1}{x}$	1.0559 ...

The cosine of an angle

To obtain the cosine of any angle enter the angle and press the cosine key.

cos 57.34° = 0.5397
cos 177.84° = −0.9993
cos 48° 41′ 22″ = 48.69° = 0.6601
cos 3.1924 radians = −0.9987

The normal calculator will give only one value of θ for any given value of cos θ.

$$\cos \theta = 0.7196 \text{ gives } \theta = 43.98°$$

As shown below the cosine curve is periodic with a period of 360°.

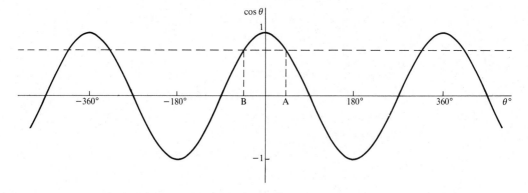

Hence when cos θ = 0.7196

$$\theta = 43.98° \text{ (A) } \pm 360n°$$

But also

$$\theta = -43.98° \text{ (B) } \pm 360n°$$

where n is zero or an integer.

Hence in all cases if the angle given by the calculator is $\alpha°$

then $\theta = \alpha° \pm 360n°$

or $\theta = -\alpha° \pm 360n°$

The *secant* of an angle is the reciprocal of the cosine of the angle. Thus

$$\sec \theta = \frac{1}{\cos \theta}$$

Example Find sec 21.84°

$$\sec 21.84° = \frac{1}{\cos 21.84°} = 1.0773$$

The method when using a calculator is:

Input	Display
21.84	21.84
cos	0.9282 ...
$\frac{1}{x}$	1.0773 ...

The tangent of an angle

The tangent curve is periodic with a period of 180° as shown below.

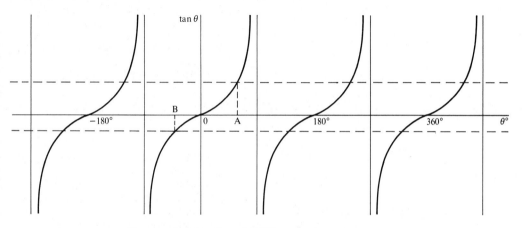

Hence when $\tan \theta = 1.8921$

$$\theta = 62.14° \text{ (A)} \pm 180n°$$

Similarly when $\tan \theta = -0.9276$

$$\theta = -42.85° \text{ (B)} \pm 180n°$$

Hence in all cases if the angle given by the calculator is $\alpha°$ then

$$\theta = \alpha° \pm 180n°$$

where n is zero or an integer.

The *cotangent* of an angle is the reciprocal of the tangent of the angle. Thus

$$\cot \theta = \frac{1}{\tan \theta}$$

Example Find cot 57.82°

$$\cot 57.82° = \frac{1}{\tan 57.82°} = 0.6292 ...$$

53

Using a calculator the method is:

Input	Display
57.82	57.82
tan	1.5892 ...
$\dfrac{1}{x}$	0.6292 ...

STATISTICAL FORMULAE

Median

For a series of observations arranged in ascending (or descending) order of size the median is the middle value. If the number of observations is even the median is the mean of the two middle values.

For a frequency distribution

$$\text{median} = L + i\left(\frac{\frac{1}{2}N - c}{f}\right)$$

L = lower boundary of the median class
i = width of median class
N = total frequency
c = cumulative frequency up to median class
f = frequency of the median class

Mode

For a set of observations the mode is the value which occurs most frequently.

For a frequency distribution

$$\text{mode} = L + i\left(\frac{d_1}{d_1 + d_2}\right)$$

L = lower boundary of the modal class
i = width of modal class
d_1 = difference between frequency of modal class and frequency of next lower class
d_2 = difference between frequency of modal class and frequency of next higher class

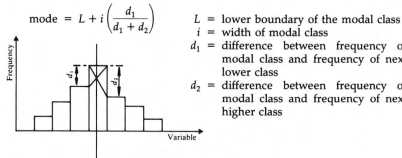

Standard deviation

$$\sigma = \sqrt{\frac{\Sigma f(x - \bar{x})^2}{N}} = \sqrt{\frac{\Sigma fx^2}{N} - \bar{x}^2}$$

Arithmetic mean

$$\bar{x} = \frac{\Sigma fx}{N}$$

x = variable
f = frequency
N = total frequency

Coded method for calculating the mean and standard deviation

$\bar{x}$ = assumed mean + $\bar{x}_c \times$ unit size

$$\bar{x}_c = \frac{\Sigma fx_c}{N}$$

$\sigma = \sigma_c \times$ unit size

$$\sigma_c = \sqrt{\frac{\Sigma fx^2_c}{N} - \bar{x}^2_c}$$

Example

Class	x	x_c	f	fx_c	fx^2_c
5.94–5.96	5.95	−5	8	−40	200
5.97–5.99	5.98	−2	37	−74	148
6.00–6.02	6.01	1	90	90	90
6.03–6.05	6.04	4	52	208	832
6.06–6.08	6.07	7	13	91	637
			200	275	1907

assumed mean = 6.00
unit size = 0.01

$$\bar{x}_c = \frac{275}{200} = 1.375$$

$$\bar{x} = 6.00 + 1.375 \times 0.01$$

$$= 6.00 + 0.01375 = 6.013\,75$$

$$\sigma_c = \sqrt{\frac{1907}{200} - (1.375)^2}$$

$$= \sqrt{9.535 - 1.891}$$

$$= \sqrt{7.644} = 2.765$$

$$\sigma = 2.765 \times 0.01 = 0.027\,65$$

Simple probability $p = \dfrac{\text{number of ways in which an event can happen}}{\text{total number of ways which are possible}}$

To find the probability of throwing a six on a die:

$$\text{number of ways in which a six can be thrown} = 1$$

$$\text{total number of ways that are possible} = 6$$

$$p = \frac{1}{6}$$

The value of a probability always lies between 0 and 1.

Addition law of probability
If two events could not happen at the same time the events are mutually exclusive.

If $p_1, p_2, p_3, \ldots$ are the separate probabilities of a set of mutually exclusive events, then the probability of one of these events occurring is

$$P = p_1 + p_2 + p_3 + \ldots$$

Multiplication law of probability
An independent event is one which has no effect on subsequent events.

If $p_1, p_2, p_3, \ldots$ are the separate probabilities of a set of independent events, then the probability of all the events occurring is

$$P = p_1 \times p_2 \times p_3 \times \ldots$$

Linear correlation
The least square line approximating to the set of points $(x_1, y_1), (x_2, y_2) \ldots (x_n, y_n)$ has the equation $y = a + bx$. The constants a and b are found by solving the simultaneous equations:

$$\Sigma y = aN + b \Sigma x \tag{1}$$

$$\Sigma xy = a \Sigma x + b \Sigma x^2 \tag{2}$$

where N is the number of points.

The coefficient of correlation is

$$r = \frac{\Sigma XY}{\sqrt{\Sigma X^2 \Sigma Y^2}} \quad \text{where } X = x - \bar{x} \text{ and } Y = y - \bar{y}$$

For perfect positive correlation $r = +1$
For perfect negative correlation $r = -1$

Least square line

The least square line approximating the set of points $(x_1, y_1), (x_2, y_2) \ldots (x_n, y_n)$ has the equation

$$y = a_0 + a_1 x$$

The constants a_0 and a_1 are found by solving the equations

$$\Sigma y = a_0 n + a_1 \Sigma x \qquad (1)$$

$$\Sigma xy = a_0 \Sigma x + a_1 \Sigma x^2 \qquad (2)$$

where n is the number of points in the set.

The amount of work involved in finding the least square line can be shortened by using

$$y = \left(\frac{\Sigma XY}{\Sigma X^2} \right) x$$

where $X = x - \bar{x}$ and $Y = y - \bar{y}$.

Control chart for sample means

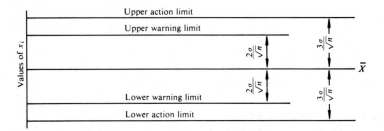

$$\bar{X} = \frac{\bar{x}_1 + \bar{x}_2 + \bar{x}_3 + \ldots \bar{x}_n}{n} \text{ where } \bar{X} = \text{overall mean and } \bar{x}_i = \text{mean of } i\text{th sample}$$

$$\bar{R} = \frac{R_1 + R_2 + R_3 + \ldots + R_n}{n} \quad \text{where } \bar{R} = \text{average range and } R_i = \text{range of } i\text{th sample}$$

$\sigma = d\bar{R}$ where d is a constant which depends upon the sample size.

Values of d

Sample size	d	Sample size	d	Sample size	d	Sample size	d	Sample size	d
2	0.8862	6	0.3946	10	0.3249	14	0.2935	18	0.2747
3	0.5908	7	0.3698	11	0.3152	15	0.2880	19	0.2711
4	0.4857	8	0.3512	12	0.3069	16	0.2831	20	0.2677
5	0.4299	9	0.3367	13	0.2998	17	0.2787		

$$\text{Warning limits} = \bar{X} \pm \frac{2\sigma}{\sqrt{n}} \qquad \text{Action limits} = \bar{X} \pm \frac{3\sigma}{\sqrt{n}}$$

The warning and action limits can also be calculated as follows:

$$\text{Warning limits} = \bar{X} \pm A_{0.025} \times \bar{R} \qquad \text{Action limits} = \bar{X} \pm A_{0.001} \times \bar{R}$$

where $\bar{R}$ is the average range of the samples and A is a constant depending upon the sample size.

56

Values of A

Sample size	$A_{0.025}$	$A_{0.001}$	Sample size	$A_{0.025}$	$A_{0.001}$
2	1.23	1.94	7	0.27	0.43
3	0.67	1.05	8	0.24	0.38
4	0.48	0.75	9	0.22	0.35
5	0.38	0.59	10	0.20	0.32
6	0.32	0.50			

Note that $A_{0.025} \times \overline{R} = \dfrac{2\sigma}{\sqrt{n}}$ and that $A_{0.001} \times \overline{R} = \dfrac{3\sigma}{\sqrt{n}}$ (approximately)

BINOMIAL COEFFICIENTS

	0	1	2	3	4	5	6	7	8	9	10
1	1	1									
2	1	2	1								
3	1	3	3	1							
4	1	4	6	4	1						
5	1	5	10	10	5	1					
6	1	6	15	20	15	6	1				
7	1	7	21	35	35	21	7	1			
8	1	8	28	56	70	56	28	8	1		
9	1	9	36	84	126	126	84	36	9	1	
10	1	10	45	120	210	252	210	120	45	10	1
11	1	11	55	165	330	462	462	330	165	55	11
12	1	12	66	220	495	792	924	792	495	220	66
13	1	13	78	286	715	1287	1716	1716	1287	715	286
14	1	14	91	364	1001	2002	3003	3432	3003	2002	1001
15	1	15	105	455	1365	3003	5005	6435	6435	5005	3003
16	1	16	120	560	1820	4368	8008	11440	12870	11440	8008
17	1	17	136	680	2380	6188	12376	19448	24310	24310	19448
18	1	18	153	816	3060	8568	18564	31824	43758	48620	43758
19	1	19	171	969	3876	11628	27132	50388	75582	92378	92378
20	1	20	190	1140	4845	15504	38760	77520	125970	167960	184756

$(a + b)^5 = a^5 + 5a^4b + 10a^3b^2 + 10a^2b^3 + 5ab^4 + b^5.$

Note that the coefficients are symmetrical. Thus

$(a + b)^{15} = a^{15} + 15a^{14}b + 105a^{13}b^2 + 455a^{12}b^3 + 1365a^{11}b^4 + 3003a^{10}b^5 + 5005a^9b^6$

$\qquad + 6435a^8b^7 + 6435a^7b^8 + 5005a^6b^9 + 3003a^5b^{10} + 1365a^4b^{11} + 455a^3b^{12}$

$\qquad + 105a^2b^{13} + 15ab^{14} + b^{15}.$

Binomial distribution

If the probability of finding a defective item in a single trial is p then the probability of finding $0, 1, 2, 3 \ldots$ defective items in a sample of n items is the successive terms of the expansion of $(q + p)^n$, where $q = 1 - p$. Note that p is the fraction of defective items produced by the process.

Number of defective items in the sample	0	1	2
Probability	q^n	$nq^{n-1}p$	$\dfrac{n(n-1)}{2!}q^{n-2}p^2$

57

Approximations to the binomial distribution

(i) If np is less than 5 then the binomial distribution is well approximated by the Poisson distribution with $\lambda = np$.

(ii) If np is greater than 5 then the binomial distribution may be approximated by a normal distribution with $\bar{x} = np$ and $\sigma = \sqrt{npq}$

POISSON DISTRIBUTION

χ	0.1	0.2	0.3	0.4	0.5	0.6	0.7	0.8	0.9	1.0
0	0.9048	0.8187	0.7408	0.6703	0.6065	0.5488	0.4966	0.4493	0.4066	0.3679
1	0.0905	0.1637	0.2222	0.2681	0.3033	0.3293	0.3476	0.3595	0.3659	0.3679
2	0.0045	0.0164	0.0333	0.0536	0.0758	0.0988	0.1217	0.1438	0.1647	0.1839
3	0.0002	0.0011	0.0033	0.0072	0.0126	0.0198	0.0284	0.0383	0.0494	0.0613
4	0.0000	0.0001	0.0002	0.0007	0.0016	0.0030	0.0050	0.0077	0.0111	0.0153
5	0.0000	0.0000	0.0000	0.0001	0.0002	0.0004	0.0007	0.0012	0.0020	0.0031
6	0.0000	0.0000	0.0000	0.0000	0.0000	0.0000	0.0001	0.0002	0.0003	0.0005
7	0.0000	0.0000	0.0000	0.0000	0.0000	0.0000	0.0000	0.0000	0.0000	0.0001

χ	1.1	1.2	1.3	1.4	1.5	1.6	1.7	1.8	1.9	2.0
0	0.3329	0.3012	0.2725	0.2466	0.2231	0.2019	0.1827	0.1653	0.1496	0.1353
1	0.3662	0.3614	0.3543	0.3452	0.3347	0.3230	0.3106	0.2975	0.2842	0.2707
2	0.2014	0.2169	0.2303	0.2417	0.2510	0.2584	0.2640	0.2678	0.2700	0.2707
3	0.0738	0.0867	0.0998	0.1128	0.1255	0.1378	0.1496	0.1607	0.1710	0.1804
4	0.0203	0.0260	0.0324	0.0395	0.0471	0.0551	0.0636	0.0723	0.0812	0.0902
5	0.0045	0.0062	0.0084	0.0111	0.0141	0.0176	0.0216	0.0260	0.0309	0.0361
6	0.0008	0.0012	0.0018	0.0026	0.0035	0.0047	0.0061	0.0078	0.0098	0.0120
7	0.0001	0.0002	0.0003	0.0005	0.0008	0.0011	0.0015	0.0020	0.0027	0.0034
8	0.0000	0.0000	0.0001	0.0001	0.0001	0.0002	0.0003	0.0005	0.0006	0.0009
9	0.0000	0.0000	0.0000	0.0000	0.0000	0.0000	0.0001	0.0001	0.0001	0.0002

χ	2.1	2.2	2.3	2.4	2.5	2.6	2.7	2.8	2.9	3.0
0	0.1225	0.1108	0.1003	0.0907	0.0821	0.0743	0.0672	0.0608	0.0550	0.0498
1	0.2572	0.2438	0.2306	0.2177	0.2052	0.1931	0.1815	0.1703	0.1596	0.1494
2	0.2700	0.2681	0.2652	0.2613	0.2565	0.2510	0.2450	0.2384	0.2314	0.2240
3	0.1890	0.1966	0.2033	0.2090	0.2138	0.2176	0.2205	0.2225	0.2237	0.2240
4	0.0992	0.1082	0.1169	0.1254	0.1336	0.1414	0.1488	0.1557	0.1622	0.1680
5	0.0417	0.0476	0.0538	0.0602	0.0668	0.0735	0.0804	0.0872	0.0940	0.1008
6	0.0146	0.0174	0.0206	0.0241	0.0278	0.0319	0.0362	0.0407	0.0455	0.0504
7	0.0044	0.0055	0.0068	0.0083	0.0099	0.0118	0.0139	0.0163	0.0188	0.0216
8	0.0011	0.0015	0.0019	0.0025	0.0031	0.0038	0.0047	0.0057	0.0068	0.0081
9	0.0003	0.0004	0.0005	0.0007	0.0009	0.0011	0.0014	0.0018	0.0022	0.0027
10	0.0001	0.0001	0.0001	0.0002	0.0002	0.0003	0.0004	0.0005	0.0006	0.0008
11	0.0000	0.0000	0.0000	0.0000	0.0000	0.0001	0.0001	0.0001	0.0002	0.0002
12	0.0000	0.0000	0.0000	0.0000	0.0000	0.0000	0.0000	0.0000	0.0000	0.0001

Entries in the table give the probabilities that an event will occur χ times when the average number of occurrences is λ.

POISSON DISTRIBUTION

χ	3.1	3.2	3.3	3.4	3.5	3.6	3.7	3.8	3.9	4.0
0	0.0450	0.0408	0.0369	0.0334	0.0302	0.0273	0.0247	0.0224	0.0202	0.0183
1	0.1397	0.1304	0.1217	0.1135	0.1057	0.0984	0.0915	0.0850	0.0789	0.0733
2	0.2165	0.2087	0.2008	0.1929	0.1850	0.1771	0.1692	0.1615	0.1539	0.1465
3	0.2237	0.2226	0.2209	0.2186	0.2158	0.2125	0.2087	0.2046	0.2001	0.1954
4	0.1734	0.1781	0.1823	0.1858	0.1888	0.1912	0.1931	0.1944	0.1951	0.1954
5	0.1075	0.1140	0.1203	0.1264	0.1322	0.1377	0.1429	0.1477	0.1522	0.1563
6	0.0555	0.0608	0.0662	0.0716	0.0771	0.0826	0.0881	0.0936	0.0989	0.1042
7	0.0246	0.0278	0.0312	0.0348	0.0385	0.0425	0.0466	0.0508	0.0551	0.0595
8	0.0095	0.0111	0.0129	0.0148	0.0169	0.0191	0.0215	0.0241	0.0269	0.0298
9	0.0033	0.0040	0.0047	0.0056	0.0066	0.0076	0.0089	0.0102	0.0116	0.0132
10	0.0010	0.0013	0.0016	0.0019	0.0023	0.0028	0.0033	0.0039	0.0045	0.0053
11	0.0003	0.0004	0.0005	0.0006	0.0007	0.0009	0.0011	0.0013	0.0016	0.0019
12	0.0001	0.0001	0.0001	0.0002	0.0002	0.0003	0.0003	0.0004	0.0005	0.0006
13	0.0000	0.0000	0.0000	0.0000	0.0001	0.0001	0.0001	0.0001	0.0002	0.0002
14	0.0000	0.0000	0.0000	0.0000	0.0000	0.0000	0.0000	0.0000	0.0000	0.0001

χ	4.1	4.2	4.3	4.4	4.5	4.6	4.7	4.8	4.9	5.0
0	0.0166	0.0150	0.0136	0.0123	0.0111	0.0101	0.0091	0.0082	0.0074	0.0067
1	0.0679	0.0630	0.0583	0.0540	0.0500	0.0462	0.0427	0.0395	0.0365	0.0337
2	0.1393	0.1323	0.1254	0.1188	0.1125	0.1063	0.1005	0.0948	0.0894	0.0842
3	0.1904	0.1852	0.1798	0.1743	0.1687	0.1631	0.1574	0.1517	0.1460	0.1404
4	0.1951	0.1944	0.1933	0.1917	0.1898	0.1875	0.1849	0.1820	0.1789	0.1755
5	0.1600	0.1633	0.1662	0.1687	0.1708	0.1725	0.1738	0.1747	0.1753	0.1755
6	0.1093	0.1143	0.1191	0.1237	0.1281	0.1323	0.1362	0.1398	0.1432	0.1462
7	0.0640	0.0686	0.0732	0.0778	0.0824	0.0869	0.0914	0.0959	0.1002	0.1044
8	0.0328	0.0360	0.0393	0.0428	0.0463	0.0500	0.0537	0.0575	0.0614	0.0653
9	0.0150	0.0168	0.0188	0.0209	0.0232	0.0255	0.0280	0.0307	0.0334	0.0363
10	0.0061	0.0071	0.0081	0.0092	0.0104	0.0118	0.0132	0.0147	0.0164	0.0181
11	0.0023	0.0027	0.0032	0.0037	0.0043	0.0049	0.0056	0.0064	0.0073	0.0082
12	0.0008	0.0009	0.0011	0.0014	0.0016	0.0019	0.0022	0.0026	0.0030	0.0034
13	0.0002	0.0003	0.0004	0.0005	0.0006	0.0007	0.0008	0.0009	0.0011	0.0013
14	0.0001	0.0001	0.0001	0.0001	0.0002	0.0002	0.0003	0.0003	0.0004	0.0005
15	0.0000	0.0000	0.0000	0.0000	0.0001	0.0001	0.0001	0.0001	0.0001	0.0002

Entries in the table give the probabilities that an event will occur χ times when the average number of occurrences is λ.

If λ is the expected number of defective items in a sample then the probabilities of finding 0, 1, 2, 3 . . . defective items in the sample is given by the successive terms of the expansion of $e^{-\lambda}e^{\lambda}$.

Number of defective items in the sample	0	1	2
Probability	$e^{-\lambda}$	$\lambda e^{-\lambda}$	$\dfrac{\lambda^2}{2!}e^{-\lambda}$

NORMAL DISTRIBUTION

u	0.00	0.01	0.02	0.03	0.04	0.05	0.06	0.07	0.08	0.09
0.0	0.50000	0.49601	0.49202	0.48803	0.48405	0.48006	0.47608	0.47210	0.46812	0.46414
0.1	0.46017	0.45620	0.45224	0.44828	0.44433	0.44038	0.43644	0.43250	0.42858	0.42465
0.2	0.42074	0.41683	0.41294	0.40905	0.40517	0.40129	0.39743	0.39358	0.38974	0.38591
0.3	0.38209	0.37828	0.37448	0.37070	0.36693	0.36317	0.35942	0.35569	0.35197	0.34827
0.4	0.34458	0.34090	0.33724	0.33360	0.32997	0.32636	0.32276	0.31918	0.31561	0.31207
0.5	0.30854	0.30503	0.30153	0.29806	0.29460	0.29116	0.28774	0.28434	0.28096	0.27760
0.6	0.27425	0.27093	0.26763	0.26435	0.26109	0.25785	0.25463	0.25143	0.24825	0.24510
0.7	0.24196	0.23885	0.23576	0.23269	0.22965	0.22663	0.22363	0.22065	0.21770	0.21476
0.8	0.21186	0.20897	0.20611	0.20327	0.20045	0.19766	0.19489	0.19215	0.18943	0.18673
0.9	0.18406	0.18141	0.17879	0.17619	0.17361	0.17106	0.16853	0.16602	0.16354	0.16109
1.0	0.15866	0.15625	0.15386	0.15150	0.14917	0.14686	0.14457	0.14231	0.14007	0.13786
1.1	0.13567	0.13350	0.13136	0.12924	0.12714	0.12507	0.12302	0.12100	0.11900	0.11702
1.2	0.11507	0.11314	0.11123	0.10935	0.10749	0.10565	0.10383	0.10204	0.10027	0.09853
1.3	0.09680	0.09510	0.09342	0.09176	0.09012	0.08851	0.08692	0.08534	0.08379	0.08226
1.4	0.08076	0.07927	0.07780	0.07636	0.07493	0.07353	0.07215	0.07078	0.06944	0.06811
1.5	0.06681	0.06552	0.06426	0.06301	0.06178	0.06057	0.05938	0.05821	0.05705	0.05592
1.6	0.05480	0.05370	0.05262	0.05155	0.05050	0.04947	0.04846	0.04746	0.04648	0.04551
1.7	0.04457	0.04363	0.04272	0.04182	0.04093	0.04006	0.03920	0.03836	0.03754	0.03673
1.8	0.03593	0.03515	0.03438	0.03362	0.03288	0.03216	0.03144	0.03074	0.03005	0.02938
1.9	0.02872	0.02807	0.02743	0.02680	0.02619	0.02559	0.02500	0.02442	0.02385	0.02330
2.0	0.02275	0.02222	0.02169	0.02118	0.02068	0.02018	0.01970	0.01923	0.01876	0.01831
2.1	0.01786	0.01743	0.01700	0.01659	0.01618	0.01578	0.01539	0.01500	0.01463	0.01426
2.2	0.01390	0.01355	0.01321	0.01287	0.01255	0.01222	0.01191	0.01160	0.01130	0.01101
2.3	0.01072	0.01044	0.01017	0.00990	0.00964	0.00939	0.00914	0.00889	0.00866	0.00842
2.4	0.00820	0.00798	0.00776	0.00755	0.00734	0.00714	0.00695	0.00676	0.00657	0.00639
2.5	0.00621	0.00604	0.00587	0.00570	0.00554	0.00539	0.00523	0.00508	0.00494	0.00480
2.6	0.00466	0.00453	0.00440	0.00427	0.00415	0.00402	0.00391	0.00379	0.00368	0.00357
2.7	0.00347	0.00336	0.00326	0.00317	0.00307	0.00298	0.00289	0.00280	0.00272	0.00264
2.8	0.00256	0.00248	0.00240	0.00233	0.00226	0.00219	0.00212	0.00205	0.00199	0.00193
2.9	0.00187	0.00181	0.00175	0.00169	0.00164	0.00159	0.00154	0.00149	0.00144	0.00139
3.0	0.00135	0.00131	0.00126	0.00122	0.00118	0.00114	0.00111	0.00107	0.00104	0.00100
3.1	0.00097	0.00094	0.00090	0.00087	0.00084	0.00082	0.00079	0.00076	0.00074	0.00071
3.2	0.00069	0.00066	0.00064	0.00062	0.00060	0.00058	0.00056	0.00054	0.00052	0.00050
3.3	0.00048	0.00047	0.00045	0.00043	0.00042	0.00040	0.00039	0.00038	0.00036	0.00035
3.4	0.00034	0.00032	0.00031	0.00030	0.00029	0.00028	0.00027	0.00026	0.00025	0.00024
3.5	0.00023	0.00022	0.00022	0.00021	0.00020	0.00019	0.00019	0.00018	0.00017	0.00017
3.6	0.00016	0.00015	0.00015	0.00014	0.00014	0.00013	0.00013	0.00012	0.00012	0.00011
3.7	0.00011	0.00010	0.00010	0.00010	0.00009	0.00009	0.00008	0.00008	0.00008	0.00008
3.8	0.00007	0.00007	0.00007	0.00006	0.00006	0.00006	0.00006	0.00005	0.00005	0.00005
3.9	0.00005	0.00005	0.00004	0.00004	0.00004	0.00004	0.00004	0.00004	0.00003	0.00003

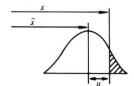

$$u = \frac{x - \bar{x}}{\sigma}$$

x = value of the variate
$\bar{x}$ = arithmetic mean
σ = standard deviation

Relation between the binomial, Poisson and normal distributions

If $n > 50$ and $\lambda = np < 5$ then the binomial distribution is very closely approximated by the Poisson distribution.

If $n = 50$ and $\lambda = np > 5$ then the binomial distribution is well approximated by the normal distribution with $\bar{x} = np$ and $\sigma = \sqrt{npq}$.

PERCENTAGE POINTS OF THE *t*-DISTRIBUTION

One sided test

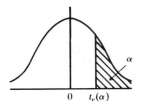

$$0 \quad t_\nu(\alpha)$$

$Pr(T_\nu > t_\nu(\alpha)) = \alpha,$
for ν degrees of freedom

Two sided test

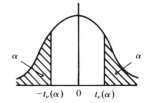

$$-t_\nu(\alpha) \quad 0 \quad t_\nu(\alpha)$$

$Pr(T_\nu > t_\nu(\alpha) \text{ and } T_\nu < t_\nu(\alpha)) = 2\alpha,$
for ν degrees of freedom

ν	α=0.4 2α=0.8	0.25 0.5	0.1 0.2	0.05 0.1	0.025 0.05	0.01 0.02	0.005 0.01	0.0025 0.005	0.001 0.002	0.0005 0.001
1	0.325	1.000	3.078	6.314	12.706	31.821	63.657	127.320	318.310	636.620
2	0.289	0.816	1.886	2.920	4.303	6.965	9.925	14.089	22.327	31.598
3	0.277	0.765	1.638	2.353	3.182	4.541	5.841	7.453	10.214	12.924
4	0.271	0.741	1.533	2.132	2.776	3.747	4.604	5.598	7.173	8.610
5	0.267	0.727	1.476	2.015	2.571	3.365	4.032	4.773	5.893	6.869
6	0.265	0.718	1.440	1.943	2.447	3.143	3.707	4.317	5.208	5.959
7	0.263	0.711	1.415	1.895	2.365	2.998	3.499	4.029	4.785	5.408
8	0.262	0.706	1.397	1.860	2.306	2.896	3.355	3.833	4.501	5.041
9	0.261	0.703	1.383	1.833	2.262	2.821	3.250	3.690	4.297	4.781
10	0.260	0.700	1.372	1.812	2.228	2.764	3.169	3.581	4.144	4.587
11	0.260	0.697	1.363	1.796	2.201	2.718	3.106	3.497	4.025	4.437
12	0.259	0.695	1.356	1.782	2.179	2.681	3.055	3.428	3.930	4.318
13	0.259	0.694	1.350	1.771	2.160	2.650	3.012	3.372	3.852	4.221
14	0.258	0.692	1.345	1.761	2.145	2.624	2.977	3.326	3.787	4.140
15	0.258	0.691	1.341	1.753	2.131	2.602	2.947	3.286	3.733	4.073
16	0.258	0.690	1.337	1.746	2.120	2.583	2.921	3.252	3.686	4.015
17	0.257	0.689	1.333	1.740	2.110	2.567	2.898	3.222	3.646	3.965
18	0.257	0.688	1.330	1.734	2.101	2.552	2.878	3.197	3.610	3.922
19	0.257	0.688	1.328	1.729	2.093	2.539	2.861	3.174	3.579	3.883
20	0.257	0.687	1.325	1.725	2.086	2.528	2.845	3.153	3.552	3.850
21	0.257	0.686	1.323	1.721	2.080	2.518	2.831	3.135	3.527	3.819
22	0.256	0.686	1.321	1.717	2.074	2.508	2.819	3.119	3.505	3.792
23	0.256	0.685	1.319	1.714	2.069	2.500	2.807	3.104	3.485	3.767
24	0.256	0.685	1.318	1.711	2.064	2.492	2.797	3.091	3.467	3.745
25	0.256	0.684	1.316	1.708	2.060	2.485	2.787	3.078	3.450	3.725
26	0.256	0.684	1.315	1.706	2.056	2.479	2.779	3.067	3.435	3.707
27	0.256	0.684	1.314	1.703	2.052	2.473	2.771	3.057	3.421	3.690
28	0.256	0.683	1.313	1.701	2.048	2.467	2.763	3.047	3.408	3.674
29	0.256	0.683	1.311	1.699	2.045	2.462	2.756	3.038	3.396	3.659
30	0.256	0.683	1.310	1.697	2.042	2.457	2.750	3.030	3.385	3.646
40	0.255	0.681	1.303	1.684	2.021	2.423	2.704	2.971	3.307	3.551
60	0.254	0.679	1.296	1.671	2.000	2.390	2.660	2.915	3.232	3.460
120	0.254	0.677	1.289	1.658	1.980	2.358	2.617	2.860	3.160	3.373
∞	0.253	0.674	1.282	1.645	1.960	2.326	2.576	2.807	3.090	3.291

Example If T is a random variable having a *t*-distribution with 10 degrees of freedom, what is the value t such that the probability that $t > T$ is 0.05?

If $T \sim t_{10}$ we require the value t such that

$$Pr(T > t | \nu = 10) = 0.05$$

where $t = 1.812$

61

PERCENTAGE POINTS OF THE χ^2 DISTRIBUTION

The values tabulated are $\chi^2_\nu(\alpha)$, where
$Pr(\chi^2_\nu > \chi^2_\nu(\alpha)) = \alpha$, for ν degrees of freedom.

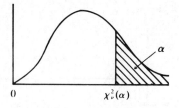

α ν	0.995	0.990	0.975	0.950	0.900	0.750	0.500
1	392704.10^{-10}	157088.10^{-9}	982069.10^{-9}	393214.10^{-8}	0.0157908	0.1015308	0.454936
2	0.0100251	0.0201007	0.0506356	0.102587	0.210721	0.575364	1.38629
3	0.0717218	0.114832	0.215795	0.351846	0.584374	1.212534	2.36597
4	0.206989	0.297109	0.484419	0.710723	1.063623	1.92256	3.35669
5	0.411742	0.554298	0.831212	1.145476	1.61031	2.67460	4.35146
6	0.675727	0.872090	1.23734	1.63538	2.20413	3.45460	5.34812
7	0.989256	1.239043	1.68987	2.16735	2.83311	4.25485	6.34581
8	1.34441	1.64650	2.17973	2.73264	3.48954	5.07064	7.34412
9	1.73493	2.08790	2.70039	3.32511	4.16816	5.89883	8.34283
10	2.15586	2.55821	3.24697	3.94030	4.86518	6.73720	9.34182
11	2.60322	3.05348	3.81575	4.57481	5.57778	7.58414	10.3410
12	3.07382	3.57057	4.40379	5.22603	6.30380	8.43842	11.3403
13	3.56503	4.10692	5.00875	5.89186	7.04150	9.29907	12.3398
14	4.07467	4.66043	5.62873	6.57063	7.78953	10.1653	13.3393
15	4.60092	5.22935	6.26214	7.26094	8.54676	11.0365	14.3389
16	5.14221	5.81221	6.90766	7.96165	9.31224	11.9122	15.3385
17	5.69722	6.40776	7.56419	8.67176	10.0852	12.7919	16.3382
18	6.26480	7.01491	8.23075	9.39046	10.8649	13.6753	17.3379
19	6.84397	7.63273	8.90652	10.1170	11.6509	14.5620	18.3377
20	7.43384	8.26040	9.59078	10.8508	12.4426	15.4518	19.3374
21	8.03365	8.89720	10.28293	11.5913	13.2396	16.3444	20.3372
22	8.64272	9.54249	10.9823	12.3380	14.0415	17.2396	21.3370
23	9.26043	10.19567	11.6886	13.0905	14.8480	18.1373	22.3369
24	9.88623	10.8564	12.4012	13.8484	15.6587	19.0373	23.3367
25	10.5197	11.5240	13.1197	14.6114	16.4734	19.9393	24.3366
26	11.1602	12.1981	13.8439	15.3792	17.2919	20.8434	25.3365
27	11.8076	12.8785	14.5734	16.1514	18.1139	21.7494	26.3363
28	12.4613	13.5647	15.3079	16.9279	18.9392	22.6572	27.3362
29	13.1211	14.2565	16.0471	17.7084	19.7677	23.5666	28.3361
30	13.7867	14.9535	16.7908	18.4927	20.5992	24.4776	29.3360
40	20.7065	22.1643	24.4330	26.5093	29.0505	33.6603	39.3353
50	27.9907	29.7067	32.3574	34.7643	37.6886	42.9421	49.3349
60	35.5345	37.4849	40.4817	43.1880	46.4589	52.2938	59.3347
70	43.2752	45.4417	48.7576	51.7393	55.3289	61.6983	69.3345
80	51.1719	53.5401	57.1532	60.3915	64.2778	71.1445	79.3343
90	59.1963	61.7541	65.6466	69.1260	73.2911	80.6247	89.3342
100	67.3276	70.0649	74.2219	77.9295	82.3581	90.1332	99.3341

PERCENTAGE POINTS OF THE χ^2 DISTRIBUTION

For $v > 30$ take $\chi^2_v(\alpha) = v\left[1 - \dfrac{2}{9v} + u_\alpha \sqrt{\dfrac{2}{9v}}\right]^3$ where u_α is such that $Pr(U > u_\alpha) = \alpha$, and $U \sim N(0, 1)$.

α \\ v	0.250	0.100	0.050	0.025	0.010	0.005	0.001
1	1.32330	2.70554	3.84146	5.02389	6.63490	7.87944	10.828
2	2.77259	4.60517	5.99146	7.37776	9.21034	10.5966	13.816
3	4.10834	6.25139	7.81473	9.34840	11.3449	12.8382	16.266
4	5.38527	7.77944	9.48773	11.1433	13.2767	14.8603	18.467
5	6.62568	9.23636	11.0705	12.8325	15.0863	16.7496	20.515
6	7.84080	10.6446	12.5916	14.4494	16.8119	18.5476	22.458
7	9.03715	12.0170	14.0671	16.0128	18.4753	20.2777	24.322
8	10.2189	13.3616	15.5073	17.5345	20.0902	21.9550	26.125
9	11.3888	14.6837	16.9190	19.0228	21.6660	23.5894	27.877
10	12.5489	15.9872	18.3070	20.4832	23.2093	25.1882	29.588
11	13.7007	17.2750	19.6751	21.9200	24.7250	26.7568	31.264
12	14.8454	18.5493	21.0261	23.3367	26.2170	28.2995	32.909
13	15.9839	19.8119	22.3620	24.7356	27.6882	29.8195	34.528
14	17.1169	21.0641	23.6848	26.1189	29.1412	31.3194	36.123
15	18.2451	22.3071	24.9958	27.4884	30.5779	32.8013	37.697
16	19.3689	23.5418	26.2962	28.8454	31.9999	34.2672	39.252
17	20.4887	24.7690	27.5871	30.1910	33.4087	35.7185	40.790
18	21.6049	25.9894	28.8693	31.5264	34.8053	37.1565	42.312
19	22.7178	27.2036	30.1435	32.8523	36.1909	38.5823	43.820
20	23.8277	28.4120	31.4104	34.1696	37.5662	39.9968	45.315
21	24.9348	29.6151	32.6706	35.4789	38.9322	41.4011	46.797
22	26.0393	30.8133	33.9244	36.7807	40.2894	42.7957	48.268
23	27.1413	32.0069	35.1725	38.0756	41.6384	44.1813	49.728
24	28.2412	33.1962	36.4150	39.3641	42.9798	45.5585	51.179
25	29.3389	34.3816	37.6525	40.6465	44.3141	46.9279	52.618
26	30.4346	35.5632	38.8851	41.9232	45.6417	48.2899	54.052
27	31.5284	36.7412	40.1133	43.1945	46.9629	49.6449	55.476
28	32.6205	37.9159	41.3371	44.4608	48.2782	50.9934	56.892
29	33.7109	39.0875	42.5570	45.7223	49.5879	52.3356	58.301
30	34.7997	40.2560	43.7730	46.9792	50.8922	53.6720	59.703
40	45.6160	51.8051	55.7585	59.3417	63.6907	66.7660	73.402
50	56.3336	63.1671	67.5048	71.4202	76.1539	79.4900	86.661
60	66.9815	74.3970	79.0819	83.2977	88.3794	91.9517	99.607
70	77.5767	85.5270	90.5312	95.0232	100.425	104.215	112.317
80	88.1303	96.5782	101.879	106.629	112.329	116.321	124.839
90	98.6499	107.565	113.145	118.136	124.116	128.299	137.208
100	109.141	118.498	124.342	129.561	135.807	140.169	149.449

APPLIED MATHEMATICS

Composition of vectors

If the angle between two vectors is θ and their magnitudes are a and b, the magnitude of the resultant is:

$$R = \sqrt{a^2 + b^2 + 2ab \cos \theta}$$

Triangle of forces

If three forces acting at a point are in equilibrium, the vectors representing the forces form, when added, a closed triangle. In order to be in equilibrium, three non-parallel forces must be concurrent.

Polygon of forces

If four or more forces acting at a point are in equilibrium, the vectors representing the forces form, when added, a closed polygon.

Principle of moments

For equilibrium, the sum of the clockwise moments is equal to the sum of the anti-clockwise moments about any point.

Moment

$M = Fd$ M = moment of force (N m)
F = force (N)
d = distance measured perpendicular to the line of action of the force (m)

Conditions of equilibrium

The sum of the horizontal forces must be zero $\Sigma F_H = 0$

The sum of the vertical forces must be zero $\Sigma F_V = 0$

The sum of the moments must be zero $\Sigma M = 0$

Lami's theorem

If the three forces P, Q and R are in equilibrium then

$$\frac{P}{\sin \alpha} = \frac{Q}{\sin \beta} = \frac{R}{\sin \gamma}$$

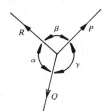

Friction

$$\mu = \frac{F}{N} = \tan \lambda$$

μ = coefficient of friction (no units)
F = force required to move one surface over another (N)
N = force pressing the surfaces together (N)
λ = the angle of friction

At all times $F \leqslant \mu N$.

Hooke's Law

Elastic strings and springs obey Hooke's Law

$$T = \lambda \frac{x}{a}$$

(λ is equal to the force required to double the length of the string or spring)

T = tension in the string (N)
x = extension (or compression)
a = natural length
λ = modulus of elasticity (N)

The work done in stretching an elastic string is $W = \dfrac{\lambda x^2}{2a}$

(The work done in compressing a spring an amount x is given by the same expression.)

MECHANICS

Linear motion

$$v_f = v_i + at$$

$$s = v_i t + \tfrac{1}{2}at^2$$

$$s = \left(\frac{v_i + v_f}{2}\right)t$$

$$v_f^2 = v_i^2 + 2as$$

v_f = final speed (m s^{-1})
v_i = initial speed (m s^{-1})
a = acceleration (m s^{-2})
t = time (s)
s = distance (m)

Circular motion

$$\omega_f = \omega_i + \alpha t$$

$$\theta = \omega_i t + \tfrac{1}{2}\alpha t^2$$

$$\theta = \left(\frac{\omega_i + \omega_f}{2}\right)t$$

$$\omega_f^2 = \omega_i^2 + 2\alpha\theta$$

ω_f = final speed (rad s^{-1})
ω_i = initial speed (rad s^{-1})
α = angular acceleration (rad s^{-2})
t = time (s)
θ = angle turned (rad)

Centripetal acceleration

$$\frac{v^2}{r} = \omega^2 r$$

Centrifugal force

$$\frac{mv^2}{r} = m\omega^2 r$$

m = mass rotating (kg)
v = tangential speed (m s^{-1})
r = radius (m)
ω = circular speed (rad s^{-1})

Momentum

$$mv$$

m = mass (kg)
v = speed (m s^{-1})

Force of a jet of water on a stationary flat plate

$$F = \rho A v^2$$

ρ = density (kg m^{-3})
A = area of jet (m^2)
v = speed of jet (m s^{-1})

Force of a jet of water on a semi-circular stationary vane

$$F = 2\rho A v^2$$

Work done

$$W = Fs$$

$$W = T\theta$$

W = work done (J)
F = force moving object (N)
s = distance moved in direction of force (m)
T = torque (N m)
θ = angle turned (rad)

Power

$$P = \frac{Fs}{t} = Fv = \frac{T\theta}{t} = 2\pi NT$$

P = power (W)
v = velocity (m s^{-1})
N = circular speed (rev s^{-1})

Energy

Potential energy (W) $= mgh$

Kinetic energy (W) $= \tfrac{1}{2}mv^2$

Change in kinetic energy (W)
$= \tfrac{1}{2}m(v_f^2 - v_i^2)$

g = acceleration due to gravity (m^2 s^{-1})
m = mass (kg)
h = height of body above datum (m)

Newton's laws of motion

Law 1 Every body will remain at rest or continue to move with uniform velocity unless an external force is applied to it.

Law 2 When an external force is applied to a body of constant mass the force produces an acceleration which is directly proportional to the force.

Law 3 Action and reaction are always equal and opposite.

Force

If a mass m increases to $m + \delta m$ whilst its speed increases from v to $v + \delta v$ in a time δt then the resultant force acting on the mass is

$$F = m\frac{dv}{dt} + v\frac{dm}{dt} \qquad (1)$$

If δm has a velocity of u before joining the mass m then

$$F = m\frac{dv}{dt} + (v - u)\frac{dm}{dt} \qquad (2)$$

If the mass of a body is constant then $\dfrac{dm}{dt} = 0$ and equations (1) and (2) reduce to

$$F = ma$$

F = force causing acceleration (N)
m = mass being accelerated (kg)
a = acceleration (m s^{-2})

Weight

$$W = mg$$

W = weight of the body (N)
m = mass of the body (kg)
g = acceleration due to gravity (m s^{-2})

Falling bodies

$$v = \sqrt{2gh}$$

v = final speed (m s^{-1})
h = height fallen through (m)

Bodies projected upwards

$$t = \frac{v}{g}$$

$$h_{max} = \frac{v^2}{2g}$$

t = time to reach greatest height (s)
v = velocity of projection (m s^{-1})
h_{max} = greatest height (m)
g = acceleration due to gravity (m s^{-2})

Impact

$$m_A v_A + m_B v_B = m_A v'_A + m_B v'_B$$

$$e = \frac{v'_A - v'_B}{v_A - v_B}$$

v = velocity before impact
v' = velocity after impact
e = coefficient of restitution

Linear impulse

$$Ft = m(v_f - v_i)$$

Vehicle on a curved horizontal track

$$v = \sqrt{g\mu r} \text{ (skidding)}$$

$$v = \sqrt{\frac{gar}{h}} \text{ (overturning)}$$

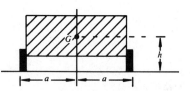

μ = coefficient of friction
r = radius of circular path

Vehicle on a curved banked track

$$v = \sqrt{gr\left(\frac{\mu + \tan\theta}{1 - \mu\tan\theta}\right)}$$

v = limiting speed for skidding

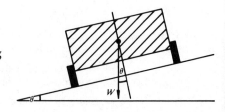

Torque

$$T = I\alpha$$

$$I = mk^2$$

T = torque (N m)
I = moment of inertia (kg m^{-2})
α = angular acceleration (rad s^{-2})
ω = angular speed (rad s^{-1})
k = radius of gyration (m)
m = mass (kg)

If a torque T acts on a body for a time t causing the angular velocity to change from ω_1 to ω_2 then

$$Tt = I(\omega_2 - \omega_1)$$

Angular momentum $= I\omega$

Kinetic energy of rotation $= \frac{1}{2}I\omega^2$

Simple harmonic motion (shm)

$$T = \frac{2\pi}{\omega}$$

$$f = \frac{1}{T} = \frac{\omega}{2\pi}$$

$$\frac{\ddot{x}}{x} = -\omega^2$$

T = periodic time (s)
f = frequency (Hz)
$\ddot{x}$ = acceleration
x = displacement
ω = circular speed (rad s^{-1})

or

Acceleration $= -\omega^2 \times$ displacement

For a spring

$$f = \frac{1}{2\pi} \sqrt{\frac{k}{m}}$$

$$f = \frac{1}{2\pi} \sqrt{\frac{g}{\delta_s}}$$

$$\delta_s = \frac{mg}{k}$$

k = spring stiffness (N m^{-1})
m = mass on spring (kg)
δ_s = deflection of spring under mass (m)

Simple pendulum

$$f = \frac{1}{2\pi} \sqrt{\frac{g}{l}}$$

l = length of pendulum (m)

Compound pendulum

$$T = 2\pi \sqrt{\frac{a^2 + k_G^2}{ag}}$$

k_G = radius of gyration through centre of mass (m)
a = distance from point of suspension to G (m)

Conical pendulum

$$T = ml\omega^2$$

T = tension in string (N)
m = mass of bob (kg)
ω = angular speed (rad s^{-1})

Motion in a vertical circle

If a mass m moves in a vertical circle of radius a and passes the lowest point of the circle with speed v_i, then as shown in the diagram

$$R - mg \cos \theta = m \frac{v^2}{a}, \text{ radially}$$

$$mg \sin \theta = -m \frac{dv}{dt}, \text{ tangentially}$$

$$\tfrac{1}{2}mv_i^2 - mga = \tfrac{1}{2}mv_f^2 - mga \cos \theta$$

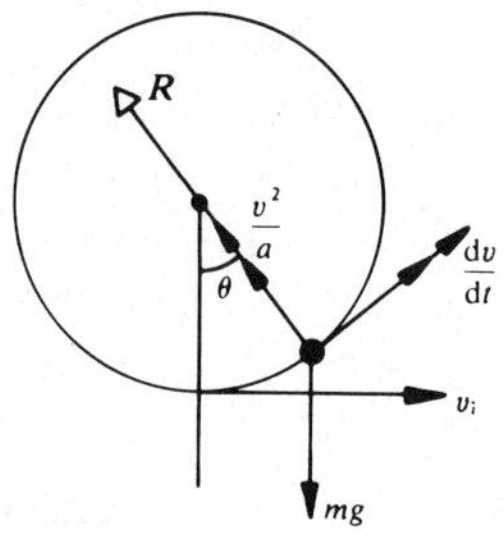

A mass restricted to a circular path will describe complete circles if $v_i^2 > 4gr$ otherwise it will come momentarily to rest before reaching the highest point of the circle and subsequently it will oscillate. If the motion is not restricted to a circular path, as in the case of a particle rotating at one end of a light string, then

$$T = m \left(\frac{v_i^2}{a} - 2g + 3g \cos \theta \right)$$

where T is the tension in the string.

If the motion is a complete circle the string is taut in the highest position and $v_i^2 \geqslant 5ga$.

For oscillations $v_i^2 \leqslant 2ga$.

The range of values for which the string goes slack is $\sqrt{2ga} < v_i < \sqrt{5ga}$.

MACHINES

$$\text{Mechanical advantage or force ratio} = \frac{\text{load}}{\text{effort}}$$

$$\text{Velocity ratio or movement ratio} = \frac{\text{distance moved by effort}}{\text{distance moved by load}}$$

$$\text{Efficiency} = \eta = \frac{\text{useful work out}}{\text{work put in}} = \frac{\text{force ratio}}{\text{movement ratio}}$$

$$\text{Movement ratio of wheel and axle} = \frac{\text{radius of wheel}}{\text{radius of axle}}$$

Movement ratio of wheel and differential axle

$$= \frac{2 \times \text{radius of wheel}}{\text{radius of larger part of axle} - \text{radius of smaller part}}$$

$$\text{Movement ratio of screw jack} = \frac{2\pi \times \text{radius at which effort is applied}}{\text{lead of screw}}$$

$$\text{Movement ratio of gear drive} = \frac{\text{number of teeth on driven wheel}}{\text{number of teeth on driver wheel}}$$

For a gear drive

$$\frac{N_A}{N_B} = \frac{n_B}{n_A}$$

N = rotation speed (rev min^{-1})
n = number of teeth on gear

For a belt drive	$$\dfrac{N_A}{N_B} = \dfrac{d_B}{d_A}$$	d = pulley diameter

Power of a belt drive	$P = v(F_1 - F_2)$ $F_1 = F_2 e^{\mu\theta}$ for flat belt $F_1 = F_2 e^{\mu\theta \cosec\,\alpha}$ for V-belt	F_1 = tension on tight side (N) F_2 = tension on slack side (N) v = linear speed of belt (m s^{-1}) P = power developed (W) θ = angle of lap (radians) μ = coefficient of friction α = angle of vee

Spirit level	$$\theta\ (\text{radians}) = \frac{\text{movement of bubble}}{R}$$ $$\theta\ (\text{degrees}) = \frac{57.3 \times \text{movement of bubble}}{R}$$	R = vial radius θ = angle of inclination of spirit level

Sine bar	$h = C \sin \alpha$	h = difference in height of plugs C = centre distance of plugs α = angular setting of sine bar

Measurement of large bores	$$D = L + \frac{\omega^2}{2L}$$	D = bore diameter L = length of gauge ω = half total amount of rock

Measurement of screw threads	$$W = D_E + d\left(1 + \cosec\frac{\alpha}{2}\right) - \frac{p}{2}\cot\frac{\alpha}{2}$$	D_E = effective diameter d = wire diameter α = flank angle

For metric threads	$W = D_E + 3d - 1.516p$ Best wire size is: $\quad d = 0.577p$	p = pitch W = diameter over wires

Tool life	$ST^n = c$ (for H.S.S. tools $n = \frac{1}{7}$ to $\frac{1}{8}$ for roughing cuts in steel and $\frac{1}{10}$ for light cuts in steel, $n = \frac{1}{5}$ when using a tungsten carbide tool for roughing cuts on steel)	S = cutting speed (m min^{-1}) T = tool life (min) n = constant c = constant

Change wheels	$$\frac{\text{number of teeth in driving gears}}{\text{number of teeth in driven wheels}} = \frac{\text{lead of thread to be cut}}{\text{pitch of lead screw}}$$	

Dividing head	$$\text{Simple indexing} = \frac{40}{n}$$ $$\text{Angular indexing} = \frac{\theta}{9}$$	n = required number of divisions θ = angle required

69

Cutting speeds in metres per minute

Material	Tool material			
	H.S.S.	Super H.S.S.	Stellite	Tungsten carbide
Aluminium alloys	70–100	90–120	over 200	over 350
Brass (free cutting)	70–100	90–120	170–250	350–500
Bronze	40–70	50–80	70–150	150–250
Copper	35–70	50–90	70–150	100–300
Iron (grey cast)	35–50	45–60	60–90	90–120
Magnesium alloys	85–135	110–150	85–135	85–135
Monel metal	15–20	18–25	25–45	50–80
Steel (high tensile)	5–10	7–12	20–35	–
Steel (mild)	35–50	45–60	70–120	–
Steel (stainless)	10–15	12–18	30–50	–
Thermo-setting plastic	35–50	45–60	70–120	100–200

$$S = \frac{\pi d N}{1000}$$

S = cutting speed (m min^{-1})
d = work or cutter diameter (mm)
N = rotational speed (rev min^{-1})

Power used in cutting

Material	k_L (N mm^{-2})	k_d	k_m (J mm^{-3})	Material	k_L (N mm^{-2})	k_d	k_m (J mm^{-3})
Aluminium	700	0.11	0.9	Mild steel	1200	0.36	2.7
Brass	1250	0.084	1.6	Tool steel	3000	0.4	7.0
Cast iron	900	0.07	1.9				

For lathework

$$P = \frac{k_L d f S}{60\ 000}$$

For drilling

$$T = k_d f^{0.75} D^{1.8}$$

$$P = \frac{2\pi N T}{60\ 000}$$

For milling

$$P = \frac{k_m d W f_m}{60}$$

Volume of metal removed

Lathework

$$V = d f S$$

Drilling

$$V = \frac{\pi D^2}{4} f N$$

Milling

$$V = \frac{W d f_m}{1000}$$

P = power used (kW)
d = depth of cut (mm)
f = feed (mm rev^{-1})
S = cutting speed (m min^{-1})
T = torque (N m)
D = drill diameter (mm)
N = rotational speed (rev min^{-1})
W = width of cut (mm)
f_m = milling machine table feed (mm min^{-1})
V = volume of metal removed (cm^3 min^{-1})
k_L = factor for lathe
k_d = factor for drilling
k_m = factor for milling

STRENGTH OF MATERIALS

$$\sigma = \frac{F}{A}$$

$$\varepsilon = \frac{x}{l}$$

$$E = \frac{\sigma}{\varepsilon} = \frac{Fl}{Ax}$$

F = applied force or load (N)
A = cross-sectional area (m^2)
σ = direct stress (N m^{-2} or Pa)
x = alteration in length
l = original length
ε = direct strain (no units)
E = Young's modulus of elasticity (N m^{-2} or Pa)

Percentage elongation = $\dfrac{\text{increase in gauge length}}{\text{original gauge length}} \times 100$

Percentage reduction in area =

$$\frac{\text{original cross-sectional area} - \text{cross-sectional area at fracture}}{\text{original cross-sectional area}} \times 100$$

Factor of safety = $\dfrac{\text{ultimate stress}}{\text{working stress}}$

$$G = \frac{\tau}{\gamma}$$

τ = shear stress (N m^{-2} or Pa)
γ = shear strain
G = modulus of rigidity (N m^{-2} or Pa)

Compound bar

$$\sigma_1 = \frac{FE_1}{E_1 A_1 + E_2 A_2} \qquad \sigma_2 = \frac{FE_2}{E_1 A_1 + E_2 A_2}$$

Temperature stress

$$\sigma = E\alpha\theta$$

α = coefficient of linear expansion
θ = change in temperature

For a compound bar:

$$(a_1 - a_2)\,\theta = F\left(\frac{1}{A_1 E_1} + \frac{1}{A_2 E_2}\right)$$

Thin cylindrical shell

$$\sigma_H = \frac{pd}{2t}$$

$$\sigma_L = \frac{pd}{4t}$$

p = internal pressure (N m^{-2} or Pa)
d = diameter of shell (m)
t = thickness of shell (m)
σ_H = hoop stress (N m^{-2} or Pa)
σ_L = longitudinal stress (N m^{-2} or Pa)

Rotating body

$$\sigma_H = \rho g \omega^2 r^2 = \rho g v^2$$

ρ = density of material (kg m^{-3})
ω = angular speed (rad s^{-1})
r = radius (m)
v = linear speed (m s^{-1})
g = gravitational acceleration (m s^{-2})

Direct strain energy

$$U = \frac{\sigma^2}{2E} \times Al$$

Shear stress

$$\tau = \frac{Q}{A}$$

Q = shearing force (N)

Bearing

$$F = \sigma_b dt$$

F = force required to cause failure (N)
d = rivet or bolt diameter (m)
t = plate thickness (m)
σ_b = ultimate bearing stress (N m^{-2} or Pa)

Beams standard cases

	Maximum bending moment	Maximum deflection	Bending moment diagram	Shear force diagram
W (point load at free end of cantilever), span l	Wl	$\dfrac{Wl^3}{3EI}$		
UDL total value W (cantilever), span l	$\dfrac{Wl}{2}$	$\dfrac{Wl^3}{8EI}$		
W (central point load, simply supported), span l	$\dfrac{Wl}{4}$	$\dfrac{Wl^3}{48EI}$		
UDL Total value W (simply supported), span l	$\dfrac{Wl}{8}$	$\dfrac{5Wl^3}{384EI}$		

UDL = Uniformly distributed load

Bending

$$\frac{M}{I} = \frac{\sigma}{y} = \frac{E}{R}$$

$$Z = \frac{I}{y}$$

$$\sigma = \frac{M}{Z}$$

M = bending moment (N m)
I = second moment of area (m^4)
σ = stress due to bending (N m^{-2} or Pa)
y = distance from neutral axis to extreme fibre (m)
Z = section modulus (m^3)
R = radius of curvature (m)
E = Young's modulus of elasticity (N m^{-2} or Pa)

Torsion

$$\frac{\tau}{r} = \frac{G\theta}{l} = \frac{T}{J}$$

θ = angle of twist in radians over a length of l metres
G = modulus of rigidity (N m^{-2} or Pa)
r = radius of shaft (m)
τ = shear stress at radius r (N m^{-2} or Pa)
T = torque (N m)
J = polar second moment of area (m^4)

Brinell hardness number (BHN)

$$= \frac{F}{A}$$

$$= \frac{F}{\frac{1}{2}\pi D \left[D - \sqrt{D - d^2}\right]}$$

Vickers pyramid number (VPN)

$$= \frac{F}{l^2/2 \sin 68°}$$

$$= \frac{1.854F}{l^2}$$

F = applied force (kg)
A = area of indentation (mm²)
D = ball diameter (mm)
d = diameter of indentation (mm)

l = average length of diagonals of indentation (mm)

Properties of sections

Section	Section modulus	Second moment of area
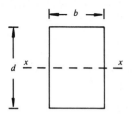	$Z_{xx} = \dfrac{bd^2}{6}$	$I_{xx} = \dfrac{bd^3}{12}$
	$Z_{xx} = \dfrac{BD^3 - bd^3}{6D}$	$I_{xx} = \dfrac{BD^3 - bd^3}{12}$
	$Z_{xx} = \dfrac{\pi D^3}{32}$	$I_{xx} = \dfrac{\pi D^4}{64}$ $I_{polar} = \dfrac{\pi D^4}{32}$
	$Z_{xx} = \dfrac{\pi}{32}\left(\dfrac{D^4 - d^4}{D}\right)$	$I_{xx} = \dfrac{\pi}{64}(D^4 - d^4)$ $I_{polar} = \dfrac{\pi}{32}(D^4 - d^4)$

Friction

$$\mu = \frac{F}{N}$$

$$\tan \phi = \mu$$

μ = coefficient of friction (no units)
F = force tending to cause sliding (N)
N = normal force (N)
ϕ = angle of repose

Coefficients of friction

Surfaces	Coefft.	Surfaces	Coefft.
Metal on metal	0.2	Hardwood on metal—dry	0.6
Rubber on metal	0.4	Hardwood on metal—slightly lubricated	0.2
Leather on metal	0.4	Rubber on a road surface	0.9

The roughness and cleanliness of the surfaces involved has a considerable effect on the coefficient of friction and values much different from the above can be easily obtained.

Friction on an incline plane, force parallel to plane

(i) When motion is about to occur up the plane

$$P = mg(\mu \cos \theta + \sin \theta)$$

(ii) When motion is about to occur down the plane

$$P = mg(\mu \cos \theta - \sin \theta)$$

Friction on an incline plane, force horizontal

(i) When motion is about to occur up the plane

$$P = mg \tan (\theta + \phi)$$

(ii) When motion is about to occur down the plane

$$P = mg \tan (\theta - \phi)$$

θ = angle of inclination of the plane to the horizontal
P = force tending to cause motion (N)

FLUIDS

$$p = \frac{F}{A}$$

$$p = p_a + \rho g h$$

p = pressure (N m^{-2})
F = force (N)
A = area (m^2)

p_a = atmospheric pressure (N m^{-2} or Pa)
ρ = density of fluid (kg m^{-3})
h = depth of fluid (m)

Centre of pressure $= \dfrac{\text{second moment of area about datum}}{\text{first moment of area about datum}}$

$$Q = Av$$

$$A_1 v_1 = A_2 v_2$$

Q = quantity flowing $(\text{m}^3 \text{ s}^{-1})$
A = area of pipe (m^2)
v = speed of flow (m s^{-1})
p = pressure $(\text{N m}^{-2}$ or Pa$)$
Z = height from datum (m)

Bernoulli's theorem

$$\frac{p_1}{\rho} + \frac{v_1^2}{2} + gZ_1 = \frac{p_2}{\rho} + \frac{v_2^2}{2} + gZ_2$$

PHYSICS DATA

Heat

Expansion of solids

$$l = l_o(1 + \alpha t)$$

l = final length
l_o = original length
α = coefficient of linear expansion
t = temperature change

Expansion of liquids and gases

$$V = V_o(1 + \beta t)$$

V_o = original volume
V = final volume
β = coefficient of cubical expansion

Boyle's law

$$p_1 V_1 = p_2 V_2$$

p = pressure $(\text{N m}^{-2}, \text{Pa})$

Charles' law

$$\frac{V_1}{T_1} = \frac{V_2}{T_2}$$

T = temperature (K)

Combination of Boyle's and Charles' law

$$\frac{p_1 V_1}{T_1} = \frac{p_2 V_2}{T_2}$$

Gas characteristic equation

$$pV = mRT$$

m = mass
R = gas constant
C = a constant
c_p = specific heat capacity at constant pressure
c_v = specific heat capacity at constant volume

Adiabatic expansion

$$pV^\gamma = C$$

$$\gamma = \frac{c_p}{c_v}$$

Polytropic expansion

$$pV^n = C$$

h_g = enthalpy of dry steam (J kg^{-1})
h_f = liquid enthalpy of steam (J kg^{-1})
h_{fg} = enthalpy of evaporation of steam (J kg^{-1})

Enthalpy of steam

$$h_g = h_f + h_{fg}$$

$$h = h_f + x h_{fg}$$

x = dryness fraction

Sound

$$v = f\lambda$$

v = velocity (m s^{-1})
f = frequency (Hz)
λ = wavelength (m)

Velocity of sound in dry air at 0°C = 331 m s^{-1}

Light

Refraction

$$n = \frac{\sin i}{\sin r}$$

n = refractive index
i = angle of incidence
r = angle of refraction

$$n = \frac{\text{real depth}}{\text{apparent depth}}$$

Lenses

The focal length of a lens is the distance between the optical centre and the principal focus.

$$m = \frac{v}{u}$$

$$\frac{1}{v} + \frac{1}{u} = \frac{1}{f}$$

m = linear magnification
v = distance of image from lens
u = distance of object from lens
f = focal length of lens

Properties of common metals

Metal	Melting point (°C)	Density (kg m^{-3})	E (G N m^{-2} or G Pa)	G (G N m^{-2} or G Pa)	Relative specific heat capacity	Coefficient of linear expansion $\times 10^{-6}$ (°C^{-1})	Resistivity at 0°C ($\mu\Omega$ m)	Resistance temp. coeff. at 0°C (K^{-1})	Electrochemical equivalent (mg C^{-1})
Aluminium	658	2700	70	27	0.21	23	24.5	0.450	0.093
Copper	1083	8900	96	38	0.09	17	15.6	0.430	0.329
Gold	1062	19300	79	27	0.03	14	20.4	0.400	0.681
Iron	1525	7850	200	82	0.11	12	89.0	0.650	0.193
Lead	327	11370	16	—	0.03	29	190.0	0.420	1.074
Mercury	−38.9	13580	—	—	0.03	60	941.0	0.100	1.039
Nickel	1452	8800	198	—	0.11	13	61.4	0.680	0.304
Platinum	1755	21040	164	51	0.03	9	98.1	0.390	0.506
Silver	960	10530	78	29	0.06	19	15.1	0.410	1.118
Tungsten	3370	19300	410	—	0.03	4.5	49.0	0.480	0.318
Zinc	418	6860	86	38	0.09	30	55.0	0.420	0.339

Properties of some copper alloys

Names and uses	Composition (%)			Condition	Mechanical properties			
	Cu	Zn	Others		Proof stress (N mm^{-2})	Tensile strength (N mm^{-2})	Elongation (%)	Hardness
Muntz metal for die stamping and extrusions	60	40	—	Extruded	110 (R_p 0.1)	350	40	H_V 75
Free cutting brass for high speed machining	58	39	Lead 3%	Extruded	140 (R_p 0.1)	440	30	H_V 100
Cartridge brass for severe cold working	70	30	—	Annealed Work hardened	75 (R_p 0.1) 500 (R_p 0.1)	310 700	70 4	H_V 65 H_V 180
Standard brass for press work	65	35	—	Annealed Work hardened	90 (R_p 0.1) 500 (R_p 0.1)	320 690	65 4	H_V 65 H_V 185
Admiralty gun-metal for general purpose castings	88	2	Tin 10%	Sand casting	130 (R_p 0.2)	270	13	H_B 70
Phosphor-bronze for castings and bushes for bearings	Remainder	0.5 max.	Tin 10% Phosphorus 0.4–1.0%	Sand casting	100 (R_p 0.2)	190	3	H_B 70–95

Cu = copper   Zn = zinc

H_V = Vickers hardness
H_B = Brinell hardness
R_p = proof stress (as a percentage)
    e.g., R_p 0.1 = 1% proof stress

Properties of cast high alloy steels to BS 3100

BS reference	Type	Composition (%)						Mechanical properties		
		C	Si	Mn	Ni	Cr	Mo	Tensile strength ($N\,mm^{-2}$)	Yield stress or proof stress ($N\,mm^{-2}$)	Elongation (%)
BW 10	Austenitic manganese steel	1.0	1.0 max.	11.0 min.	—	—	—	618–1004	—	15–40
	Possesses great hardness and hence is used for earth-moving equipment, pinions, sprockets etc. where wear resistance is required.									
410 C 21	13% chromium-steel	0.15 max.	1.0 max.	1.0 max.	1.0 max.	13.5⁄16.5	—	540	370 (R_p 0.2)	15
	Mildly corrosion resistant. Used in the paper industry.									
302 C 25	Austenitic chromium-nickel steel	0.12 max.	1.5 max.	2.0 max.	8.0 min.	17.0⁄21.0	—	480	215 (R_p 0.2)	26
	Cast stainless steel. Corrosion resistant and very ductile.									
315 C 16	Austenitic chromium-nickel-molybdenum steel	0.08 max.	1.5 max.	2.0 max.	10.0 min.	17.0⁄21.0	3.0⁄4.0	480	240	22
	Cast stainless steel with higher nickel content giving increased corrosion resistance. Molybdenum increases weldability.									
302 C 35	Heat resistant alloy steel	0.2–0.4	2.0 max.	2.0 max.	6.0⁄10.0	17.0⁄22.0	2.0 max.	600	300 (R_p 0.2)	30
334 C 11		0.75 max.	3.0 max.	2.0 max.	55⁄65	10⁄20	1.5 max.	460	270 (R_p 0.2)	3
	Can withstand temperatures in excess of 650°C. Temperature at which scaling occurs is raised by increasing amount of chromium.									

C = carbon   Si = silicon   Mn = manganese   Ni = nickel   Cr = chromium   Mo = molybdenum

Properties of medium and low alloy steels

Type	Composition (%)								Mechanical properties		Applications etc.
	C	Si	Mn	Cr	Ni	Mo	W	V	Tensile strength (N mm^{-2})	Elongation (%)	
Low alloy structural steel	0.3	0.3	0.75	—	3	—	—	—	800	26	Crankshafts, high tensile shafts etc.
Nickel-chromium-molybdenum steel	0.35	0.3	0.7	0.8	2.8	0.7	—	—	1000	16	Air hardening steel. Used at high temperatures.
High tensile steel	0.4	—	—	1.2	1.5	0.3	—	—	1800	14	Used where high strength is needed.
Spring steel	0.5	1.6	1.3	—	—	—	—	—	1500		
Steel for cutting tools	1.2	—	—	1.5	—	—	4	0.3			
Die steel	0.35	—	0.3	5.0	—	1.4	—	0.4			

W = tungsten   V = vanadium

Properties of carbon steels to BS 970 Part 1

BS reference	Composition (%)			Mechanical properties			Applications etc.
	C	Si max.	Mn	Tensile strength (N mm^{-2})	Elongation (%)	Hardness H_B	
070 M 20	0.20	0.40	0.7	400 min.	21	150	Easily machinable steels suitable for light stressing. Weldable.
070 M 26	0.26	0.40	0.7	430 min.	20	160	Stronger than 070 M 20. Good machinability and is weldable.
080 M 30	0.30	0.40	0.8	460 min.	19	165	Increased carbon increases mechanical properties but slightly less machinable.
080 M 36	0.36	0.40	0.8	490 min.	18	170	Tough steel used for forgings, nuts and bolts, levers, spanners etc.
080 M 40	0.40	0.40	0.8	510 min.	17	175	Medium carbon steel which is readily machinable.
080 M 46	0.46	0.40	0.8	550 min.	15	185	Used for motor shafts, axles, brackets and couplings.
080 M 50	0.50	0.40	0.8	570 min.	14	190	Used where strength is more important than toughness, e.g., machine tool parts.
216 M 28	0.28	0.25	1.3	550 min.	20	170	Increased manganese content gives enhanced strength and toughness.
080 M 15	0.15	0.40	0.8	460 min.	16	—	Case hardening steel. Used where wear is important, e.g., gears, pawls, etc.

C = carbon   Si = silicon   Mn = manganese

Properties of high tensile steels to BS 970 Part 2

BS reference	Type	Composition (%)								Mechanical properties		
		C	Si	Mn	Ni	Cr	Mo	Co	Ti	Tensile strength (N mm^{-2})	0.2% Proof stress (N mm^{-2})	Elongation (%)
817 M 40	Direct hardening nickel steel	0.44 max.	0.35 max.	0.7 max.	1.7 max.	1.4 max.	0.35 max.	—	—	1540	1240	8
970(897 M 39)	Direct hardening chrome-molybdenum steel	0.43 max.	0.35 max.	0.7 max.	—	3.5 max.	1.1 max.	—	—	1540	1240	7
	Maraging steels	—	—	—	18	—	3.0	8.5	0.20	1480	1400	14

C = carbon Si = silicon Mn = manganese Ni = nickel Cr = chromium Mo = molybdenum
Co = cobalt Ti = titanium

These steels are used where weight saving is important, for instance in the aircraft industry. The deep hardening types are used for plastic moulding dies, shear blades, cold drawing mandrels and pressure vessels. All these steels are difficult to machine.

Properties of stainless steels to BS 970 Part 4

BS reference	Type	Composition (%)			Mechanical properties				Applications etc.
		C	Cr	Others	0.2% Proof stress (N mm^{-2})	Tensile strength (N mm^{-2})	Elongation (%)	Hardness H_V	
410 S 21	Martensitic stainless steel	0.12	13	—	340 min.	590	20	170	Not suitable for welding or cold forming. Possesses moderate machin-
431 S 29		0.16	17	2.5% Ni	650 min.	900	11	270	ability. Used for applications where resistance to tempering at high temperatures is important e.g., turbine blades.
430 S 15	Ferritic stainless steel	0.10 max.	17	—	300	500	20 min.	165	More corrosion resistant than the martensitic steels. They are hardenable by heat-treatment. Used for presswork because of high ductility.
302 S 25	Austenitic stainless steels	0.12 max.	18	9.0% Ni	210 min.	510 min.	40	170	Possesses good resistance to corrosion, good weldability, toughness at low temperature and excellent ductility. May be hardened by cold working.

C = carbon Cr = chromium Ni = nickel

Aluminium casting alloys to BS 1490

BS reference	Type	Composition (%)		Condition	0.2% Proof stress (N mm^{-2})	Tensile strength (N mm^{-2})	Elongation (%)	Hardness (BHN)	Machinability
LM6	As cast	Copper	0.1 max.	Sand cast	60–70	160–190	5–10	50–55	Difficult
		Magnesium	0.1 max.						
		Silicon	10.0–13.0	Chill cast	70–80	190–230	7–15	55–60	Difficult
		Iron	0.6 max.						
		Manganese	0.5 max.						
		Nickel	0.1 max.	Die cast	120	280	2–5	55–60	Difficult
		Zinc	0.1 max.						
		Tin	0.5 max.						
		Lead	0.1 max.						
		Aluminium balance							
LM24		Copper	3.0–4.0	Chill cast	100–120	180–220	1.5–4	85	Fair
		Magnesium	0.1 max.						
		Silicon	7.5–9.5	Die cast	150	320	1–3	85	Fair
		Iron	1.3 max.						
		Manganese	0.5 max.						
		Nickel	0.5 max.						
		Zinc	3.0 max.						
		Tin	0.2 max.						
		Lead	0.3 max.						
		Aluminium balance							
LM25	Heat treatable	Copper	0.1 max.	Sand cast	80–100	130–150	2–3	55–65	Good
		Magnesium	0.20–0.45	Fully heat treated	200–250	230–280	0–2	90–110	Good
		Silicon	6.5–7.5						
		Iron	0.5 max.						
		Manganese	0.3 max.	Chill cast	80–100	160–200	3–6	55–65	Good
		Nickel	0.1 max.	Fully heat treated	220–260	280–320	2–5	90–110	Good
		Zinc	0.1 max.						
		Tin	0.05 max.						
		Lead	0.1 max.						
		Aluminium balance							

The above alloys are used for food and chemical plant, motor car fittings, electrical and marine castings.

Properties of wrought aluminium alloys

BS reference	Type	Composition (%)									Condition	0.2% Proof stress (N mm^{-2}) min.	Tensile strength (N mm^{-2})	Elongation (%) min.	Machinability	Cold forming
		Si	Fe	Cu	Mn	Mg	Cr	Zn	Others	Al						
1050 A	Non-heat treatable alloys	0.25	0.4	0.05	0.05	0.05	—	0.07	0.05	99.50	Annealed	—	55–95	30	Poor	Very good
											¼ hard	—	80–115	8		
											½ hard	—	100–135	6		
											¾ hard	—	135	4		
3103		0.5	0.7	0.1	0.9–1.5	0.3	0.1	0.2	0.1	Remainder	Annealed	—	90–130	24	Fair	Very good
											¼ hard	—	120–155	7		
											½ hard	—	140–175	5		
											¾ hard	—	160–195	4		
											Full hard	—	195	4		
5083		0.4	0.4	0.1	0.4–1.0	4.0–4.9	0.05–0.25	0.25	0.15	Remainder	Annealed	125	275–350	16	Good	Fair
											¼ hard	235	310–375	8		
											½ hard	270	345–405	6		
2014 A	Heat treatable alloys	0.5–0.9	0.5	3.9–5.0	0.4–1.2	0.2–0.8	0.1	0.25	0.15 + Ti 0.15	Remainder	Solution treated	245	395 min.	—	Good	Good
											Fully heat treated	355	420 min.	—	Very good	Poor
6082		0.7–1.3	0.5	0.1	0.4–1.0	0.6–1.2	0.25	0.2	0.15 + Ti 0.10	Remainder	Solution treated	115	200 min.	—	Good	Good
											Fully heat treated	240	295 min.	—	Very good	Fair

Si = silicon   Fe = iron   Cu = copper   Mn = Manganese   Mg = magnesium   Cr = chromium   Zn = zinc   Al = aluminium   Ti = titanium

Properties of grey cast irons to BS 1452

Grade	Diameter of as-cast test bar (mm)	Tensile strength min. (N mm^{-2})	Hardness H_B
150	30–32	150	160
220	30–32	220	
300	30–32	300	
400	30–32	400	

Properties of malleable irons to BS 6681

Type	Grade	Diameter of test bar (mm)	Tensile strength min. (N mm^{-2})	0.2% Proof stress min. (N mm^{-2})	Elongation min. (%)	Hardness H_B
White-heart	W 45–07	15	480	280	4	220 max.
Black-heart	B 32–10	15	320	190	10	150 max.
Pearlitic	P 55–04	15	550	340	4	180–230

Properties of nodular (S.G.) cast irons to BS 2789

Grade	Tensile strength min. (N mm^{-2})	0.2% Proof stress min. (N mm^{-2})	Elongation min. (%)	Hardness H_B	Structure
370/17	370	230	17	$\leqslant$179	Ferrite
500/7	500	310	7	170–241	Ferrite and pearlite
800/2	800	460	2	248–352	Pearlite

Properties of some thermoplastics

Name	Density (g cm^{-3})	Tensile strength (N mm^{-2})	Elongation at break (%)	Young's modulus (E) (kN mm^{-2})	Brinell hardness H_B	Machin-ability
Cellulose acetate	1.30	40	10–60	1.4	12	Excellent
Cellulose nitrate	1.35	48	40	1.4	10	Excellent
1,1-diethoxyethanes (acetals) glass filled	1.6	58–75	2–7	7	27	Good
Nylon	1.16	60	90	2.4	10	Excellent
Poly(chloroethene), (pvc) rigid	1.33	48	200	3.4	20	Excellent
Poly(ethene), (polythene) high density	1.45	20–30	20–100	0.7	2	Excellent
Poly(phenylethene), (polystyrene)	1.30	48	3	3.4	25	Fair
Poly(propene), polypropylene	1.20	27	200–700	1.3	10	Excellent
Poly(tetrafluoroethene), (ptfe)	2.10	13	100	0.3	—	Excellent

Properties of some thermosetting plastics

Name	Density (g cm^{-3})	Tensile strength (N mm^{-2})	Elongation at break (%)	Young's modulus (E) (kN mm^{-2})	Brinell hardness H_B	Machin-ability
Epoxy resin (glass filled)	1.6–2.0	68–200	4	20	38	Good
Melamine formaldehyde (fabric filled)	1.8–2.0	60–90	—	7	38	Fair
Urea formaldehyde (cellulose filled)	1.5	38–90	1	7–10	51	Fair
Phenol formaldehyde (mica filled)	1.6–1.9	38–50	0.5	17–35	36	Good

Recommendations for the turning of various plastics

Material	Condition	Depth of cut (mm)	Feed (mm rev^{-1})	Cutting speed (m min^{-1})		
				H.S.S.	Brazed carbide	Throw-away carbide tip
Thermoplastics (poly(ethene), poly(propene), tetrafluoro-ethene-fluorocarbon)	Extruded, moulded or cast	4	0.25	50	145	160
High impact phenylethene and modified acrylic	Extruded, moulded or cast	4	0.25	53	160	175
Nylon, 1,1-diethoxyethanes (acetals) and polycarbonate	Moulded	4	0.25	50	160	175
Poly(phenylethene)	Moulded or extruded	4	0.25	18	50	65
Soft grades of thermosetting plastic	Cast, moulded or filled	4	0.25	50	160	175
Hard grades of thermosetting plastic	Cast, moulded or filled	4	0.25	48	145	160

Recommendations for the drilling of various plastics

Material	Condition	Cutting speed (m min^{-1})	Feed (mm rev^{-1}) Nominal hole diameter (mm)							
			1.5	3.0	6.0	12.0	20.0	25.0	30.0	50.0
Poly(ethene), poly(propene), tetrafluoroethene-fluorocarbon	Extruded, moulded or cast	33	0.12	0.25	0.30	0.38	0.46	0.50	0.64	0.76
High impact phenylethene and modified propenoic	Extruded, moulded or cast	33	0.05	0.10	0.12	0.15	0.15	0.20	0.20	0.25
Nylon, 1,1-diethyoxyethanes (acetals) and polycarbonate	Moulded	33	0.05	0.12	0.15	0.20	0.25	0.30	0.38	0.38
Poly(phenylethene)	Moulded or extruded	66	0.03	0.05	0.08	0.10	0.13	0.15	0.18	0.20
Soft grades of thermosetting plastic	Cast, moulded or filled	50	0.08	0.13	0.15	0.20	0.25	0.30	0.38	0.38
Hard grades of thermosetting plastic	Cast, moulded or filled	33	0.05	0.13	0.15	0.20	0.25	0.30	0.38	0.38

Comparison of hardness numbers

Rockwell C scale	Vickers pyramid	Brinell	Rockwell C scale	Vickers pyramid	Brinell	Rockwell C scale	Vickers pyramid	Brinell
68	1030		49	515	468	30	299	286
67	975		48	500	458	29	291	279
66	935		47	485	447	28	284	272
65	895		46	470	436	27	277	266
64	860		45	456	426	26	271	260
63	830		44	442	416	25	265	255
62	800		43	430	406	24	260	250
61	770		42	418	396	23	255	245
60	740		41	406	386	22	250	240
59	715	609	40	395	376	21	245	235
58	690	594	39	385	366	20	240	230
57	670	579	38	375	356		220	210
56	650	564	37	365	346		200	190
55	630	549	36	355	337		180	171
54	610	534	35	345	328		160	152
53	590	519	34	335	319		140	133
52	570	504	33	325	310		120	114
51	550	492	32	315	302		100	95
50	532	480	31	307	294			

Coefficient of thermal conductivity

Substance	Coefficient (W m^{-1} K^{-1})	Substance	Coefficient (W m^{-1} K^{-1})	Substance	Coefficient (W m^{-1} K^{-1})
Silver	420	Mild steel	55	Asbestos	0.18
Copper	386	Cast iron	49	Cork	0.04
Aluminium	202	Lead	36	Felt	0.04
Duralumin	160	Concrete	0.9–1.4	Air	0.025
Brass	120	Glass	0.8–1.1	Wood	0.02
Tin	61	Brick	0.35–0.7		

$$Q = \frac{kAT}{x}$$

Q = rate of heat energy transfer
A = conducting area
T = temperature difference between two faces
x = thickness of material
k = coefficient of thermal conductivity

Calorific values of fuels

Fuel	Calorific value (MJ kg^{-1})	Fuel	Calorific value (MJ kg^{-1})	Fuel	Calorific value (MJ kg^{-1})
Carbon	33	Hydrogen	143	Refinery residuals	43
Coal (anthracite)	33–37	Kerosene	46.6	Wood (dry)	13
Coal (power station)	22.5–26.5	Natural gas	52	Other fuel oils	45–46
Coke	30	Peat	15		
Diesel oil	44	Petrol	49		

Specific heat capacity of gases

Gas	Constant pressure (c_p)	Constant volume (c_v)	Gas	Constant pressure (c_p)	Constant volume (c_v)
Air	1.005	0.712	Hydrogen	14.486	10.383
Carbon dioxide	0.837	0.653	Nitrogen	1.046	0.754
Carbon monoxide	1.046	0.750	Oxygen	0.921	0.670

Thermocouples

Type	Low limit (°C)	High limit (°C)
Copper/constantan	−250	400
Chrome/constantan	−200	700
Iron/constantan	−200	850
Chrome/alumel	0	1100
Platinum/platinum-rhodium	0	1400
Tungsten/molybdenum	1250	2600

Electrical conductivity

The table below gives the current transmitted by rods 2.54 mm in diameter and 305 mm long when a potential difference of 1 volt is applied across their ends.

Conductors		Conductors		Insulators		Insulators	
Material	Current A	Material	Current A	Material	Current A	Material	Current A
Silver	1080	Iron	166	Wood	10^{-19}	Mica	10^{-20}
Copper	982	Lead	82	Glass	10^{-19}	Hard	
Aluminium	570	Carbon	0.48	Bakelite	10^{-21}	rubber	10^{-23}

Electrolytic corrosion

Material	Potential (volts)	Material	Potential (volts)
Magnesium and its alloys	-1.60	Steel	-0.75
Zinc plating on steel	-1.10	Duralumin	-0.60
Cadmium plating on steel	-0.80	Stainless steel	-0.35
Wrought aluminium alloys	-0.75	Copper and brass	-0.25

The recommendations are:

For parts liable to wetting by sea water or normally exposed to the weather difference of potential should not exceed 0.25 V.

For interior parts which may be exposed to condensation but not to contamination by salt the difference of potential should not exceed 0.50 V.

Relative permittivity of insulators

Material	Relative permittivity	Material	Relative permittivity
Air	1.0006	Paper (dry)	2–2.5
Bakelite	4.5–5.5	Porcelain	6–7
Glass	5–10	Rubber	2–3.5
Mica	3–7		

Permittivity of free space $= 8.85 \times 10^{-12}\ \text{F m}^{-1}$

Breakdown electric stress of insulators

Material	Thickness (mm)	Dielectric strength (kV mm^{-1})	Material	Thickness (mm)	Dielectric strength (kV mm^{-1})
Air	1	4.36	Glass (density 2.5)	1	28.5
	6	3.27	Glass (density 2.5)	5	18.3
	10	2.98	Mica	0.1	61.0
Ebonite	1	50.0	Paraffin waxed paper	0.1	50.0

ELECTRICAL LAWS, DEFINITIONS AND FORMULAE

The ampere

That current which, if maintained in two straight parallel conductors of infinite length, of negligible circular cross-section, and placed 1 metre apart in a vacuum, would produce between these conductors a force of 2×10^{-7} newtons per metre length. Symbol for current is I. Symbol for amperes is A.

Ohm's law

The current in a circuit is directly proportional to the voltage and inversely proportional to the resistance providing the temperature remains constant.

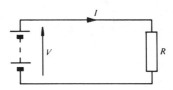

$$I = \frac{V}{R} \text{ amperes}$$

$$V = IR \text{ volts}$$

$$R = \frac{V}{I} \text{ ohms}$$

$P = VI$ watts $W = VIt$ joules

$P = I^2R$ watts $W = I^2Rt$ joules

$P = \dfrac{V^2}{R}$ watts $W = \dfrac{V^2t}{R}$ joules

$Q = It$ coulombs

$1 \text{ KW h} = 1$ Board of Trade Unit (unit) $= 3.6 \times 10^6$ joules

Resistivity

The resistance measured across the two opposite faces of a unit cube of material at a particular temperature. Symbol ρ (rho).

$R = \dfrac{\rho l}{a}$ where ρ = resistivity, l = length, a = cross-sectional area.

Resistors in series

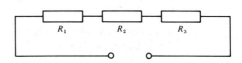

Total resistance $R_T = R_1 + R_2 + R_3$

Resistors in parallel

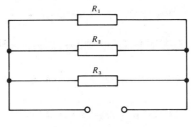

$$\frac{1}{R_T} = \frac{1}{R_1} + \frac{1}{R_2} + \frac{1}{R_3}$$

Potential divider

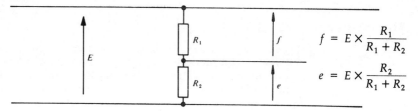

$$f = E \times \frac{R_1}{R_1 + R_2}$$

$$e = E \times \frac{R_2}{R_1 + R_2}$$

Kirchhoff's law (1)

The algebraic sum of the currents meeting at a point is zero.

$$I_1 + I_2 + I_3 - I_4 = 0$$

Kirchhoff's law (2)

The sum of the internal potential differences in a circuit equals the applied e.m.f.

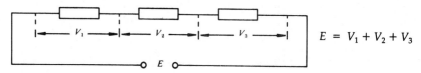

$$E = V_1 + V_2 + V_3$$

Temperature coefficient of resistance

The ratio of the increase (or decrease) of resistance per degree rise of temperature to the resistance at 0°C. Symbol α (alpha).

(i) $R_T = R_0(1 + \alpha\theta)$ General formula

(ii) $\dfrac{R_1}{R_2} = \dfrac{1 + \alpha\theta_1}{1 + \alpha\theta_2}$ θ = temperature in °C

Lenz's law

The direction of the induced e.m.f. always produces a current in a direction such as to oppose the motion or change of flux responsible for inducing that e.m.f.

The henry

If in a circuit an e.m.f. of 1 V is induced when the current changes at the rate of 1 A s^{-1} then the inductance is 1 henry. Symbol L.

Permeability of free space $= \mu_0 = 4\pi \times 10^{-7}$ H m^{-1}

Relative permeability $= \mu_r$ Absolute permeability $= \mu = \mu_0\mu_r = \dfrac{B}{H}$

B = flux density $= \dfrac{\Phi}{a}$ teslas

H = magnetic field strength

$\quad = \dfrac{IN}{l}$ amperes per metre

N = number of turns
l = length of magnetic circuit

$$\text{Reluctance} = S = \frac{l}{\mu_0 \mu_r a}$$

$$\left.\begin{array}{l}\text{Magnetic energy stored} \\ \text{in non-magnetic medium}\end{array}\right\} = \frac{B^2}{2\mu_0} \text{ joules per cubic metre}$$

$$\left.\begin{array}{l}\text{Magnetic pull between} \\ \text{two iron surfaces}\end{array}\right\} = \frac{B^2 a}{2\mu_0} \text{ newtons}$$

D.C. generators

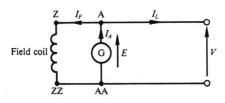 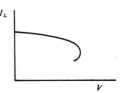

Shunt connected

$$I_A = I_L + I_F$$

$$E = V + I_a R_a$$

$$E = \frac{2p\Phi NZ}{a}$$

R = armature resistance
p = pair of poles
Φ = flux per pole in webers
N = speed in rev s^{-1}
Z = number of armature conductors
a = $2p$ for lap wound and 2 for wave wound armature

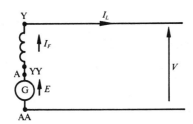 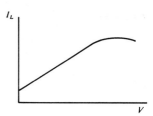

Series connected

$$I_L = I_a = I_F$$

D.C. motors

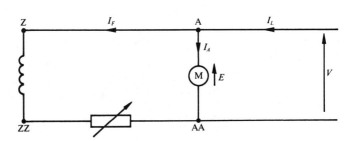

$$I_A = I_L - I_F \qquad V = E_B + I_A R_a$$

$$E_B = \frac{2P\Phi NZ}{a} \text{ (see D.C. generators)} \quad E_B \text{ is the 'back e.m.f.'}$$

To reverse direction, reverse connection A–AA *or* reverse connection Z–ZZ but not both.

$$\text{Torque} = 0.318\frac{I_a}{c}ZP\Phi \text{ newton metres} \qquad \text{Torque} \propto \Phi I_a$$

$E = L \times$ rate of change of current

$$= L \times \frac{(I_2 - I_1)}{t}$$

$$= L \frac{di}{dt} \text{ volts}$$

Also $E = N \times$ rate of change of flux

$$= N \times \frac{(\Phi_2 - \Phi_1)}{t}$$

$$= N \times \frac{d\Phi}{dt}$$

Energy stored $W = \frac{1}{2}LI^2$ joules

The farad (F)

If in a circuit a quantity of electricity of 1 coulomb is stored at a voltage of 1 volt then the capacitance is 1 farad.

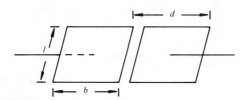

$\varepsilon_0 = 8.85 \times 10^{-12} \text{ F m}^{-1}$
$\varepsilon_r = $ relative permittivity
$n = $ number of plates
$a = $ area of plates (m^2)
$d = $ distance between plates (m)
$Q = CV$ coulombs
$W = $ electrical energy

$$a = l \times b$$

$$C = \frac{\varepsilon_0 \varepsilon_r (n - 1) a}{d} \text{ farads}$$

Energy stored $W = \frac{1}{2}CV^2$ joules

Capacitors in series

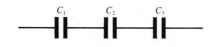

To find total capacitance

$$\frac{1}{C_T} = \frac{1}{C_1} + \frac{1}{C_2} + \frac{1}{C_3}$$

Capacitors in parallel

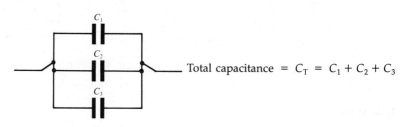

Total capacitance $= C_T = C_1 + C_2 + C_3$

A.C. theory

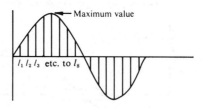

Average value of an alternating current $= \dfrac{I_1 + I_2 + I_3 + I_4 + \ldots + I_n}{n}$

For a sine wave I average $= \dfrac{1}{\pi} \displaystyle\int_0^{\pi} \sin x \, dx = 0.636 \times$ max. value.

Root mean square (r.m.s.) value $= \sqrt{\dfrac{I_1{}^2 + I_2{}^2 + I_3{}^2 + I_4{}^2 + \ldots + I_n{}^2}{n}}$

For a sine wave $= \sqrt{\dfrac{1}{2\pi} \displaystyle\int_0^{2\pi} \sin^2 x \, dx} = 0.707 \times$ max. value.

Peak or crest factor $= \dfrac{\text{peak value}}{\text{r.m.s. value}} = 1.414$ for a sine wave.

Form factor $= \dfrac{\text{r.m.s. value}}{\text{average value}} = 1.11$ for a sine wave.

A.C. and resistance

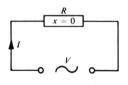 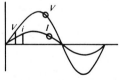

$V = V_{max} \sin \omega t$ $\omega = 2\pi f$ radians $i = I_{max} \sin \omega t$

$I = \dfrac{V}{R}$ amperes $P = I^2 R$ watts

A.C. and inductance

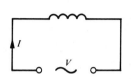 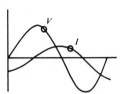 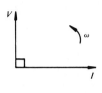

Inductive reactance $X_L = 2\pi f L$ ohms

A.C. and capacitance

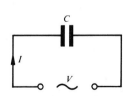 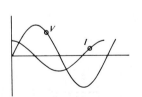 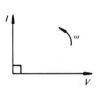

Capacitive reactance $X_C = \dfrac{1}{2\pi f C}$

Series a.c. circuit

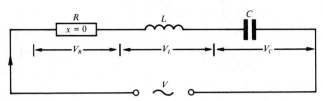

$V_R = I \times R, \quad V_L = I \times X_L, \quad V_C = I \times X_C, \quad V = \sqrt{V_R^2 + (V_L - V_C)^2}$

Phasor diagram for series a.c. circuit

As it is a series circuit I is taken as reference

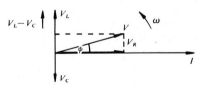

ϕ is the phase angle

Impedance triangle for series a.c. circuit

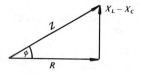

$$\cos \phi = \frac{R}{Z}$$

Apparent power = $V \times I$ volt amperes

Magnitude of impedance of circuit

$$Z = \sqrt{R^2 + (X_L - X_C)^2}$$

True power = $V \times I \times \cos \phi$ watts

$$\text{Power factor} = \frac{\text{true power}}{\text{apparent power}} = \cos \phi$$

Power triangle

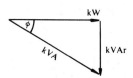

When $V_L = V_C$ and $X_L = X_C$, then $Z = R$ and voltage resonance occurs. Power factor is unity

Resonant frequency $f_r = \dfrac{1}{2\pi\sqrt{LC}}$ Hz

Q factor (voltage magnification) $= \dfrac{2\pi fL}{R} = \dfrac{1}{R}\sqrt{\dfrac{L}{C}} = \dfrac{V_L}{V}$

Parallel a.c. circuit

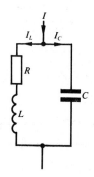

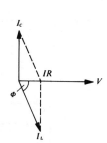

$$f_r = \frac{1}{2\pi}\sqrt{\frac{L}{C} - R^2} \text{ if } R \ll 2\pi fL \text{ then}$$

$$f_r = \frac{1}{2\pi\sqrt{LC}}$$

Dynamic impedance $CR = \dfrac{L}{CR}$

Current magnification $Q = \dfrac{2\pi fL}{R} = \dfrac{I_L}{I}$ at resonance.

Three-phase a.c. circuits

Star

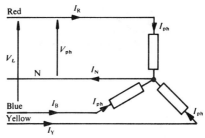

In star $I_{ph} = I_L$ $V_L = \sqrt{3}\, V_{ph}$

Neutral current I_N is the phasor sum of the three line current I_R, I_Y and I_B

$$I_N = I_R + I_Y + I_B$$

For balanced conditions $I_N = 0$

Mesh or delta

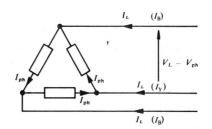

In delta $V_L = V_{ph}$
$$I_L = \sqrt{3}I_{ph}$$

Three-phase power in balanced three-phase load

$$P = \sqrt{3}\, V_L I_L \cos \phi$$

Two-wattmeter method

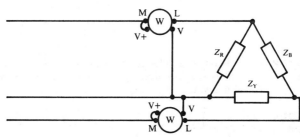

Total power $= W_1 + W_2$ $\tan \phi = \sqrt{3}\left(\dfrac{W_2 - W_1}{W_2 + W_1}\right)$

A.C. machines

Transformer

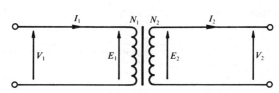

e.m.f. $E_1 = 4.44 N_1 f \Phi_m$ volts Φ_m = peak or maximum value of core flux

$E_2 = 4.44 N_2 f \Phi_m$ volts

Turns ratio $\dfrac{V_1}{V_2} \approx \dfrac{N_1}{N_2} \approx \dfrac{I_2}{I_1}$

Phasor diagram for 1:1 transformer on no-load

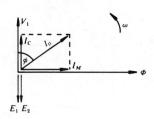

I_M = primary current component producing magnetic field

I_C = primary current component supplying hysteresis and core eddy current losses

I_0 = total primary current

$I_0 = \sqrt{I^2{}_C + I^2{}_M}$

ϕ = phase angle

$$\cos \phi = \frac{I_C}{I_0}$$

Phasor diagram for a 1:1 loaded transformer

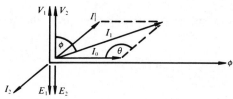

I_2 = secondary current I_1^1 = primary current due to secondary current

I_1 = total primary current   By cosine rule $(I_1)^2 = (I_0)^2 + (I_1^1)^2 - 2I_0 I_1^1 \cos \theta$
where $\theta = 180 - \Phi$ secondary

Per unit voltage regulation $= \dfrac{\text{no-load voltage} - \text{full load voltage}}{\text{no-load voltage}}$

Induction motor

Synchronous speed $N_s = \dfrac{f}{p}$ rev s^{-1} where f = frequency in hertz
p = pairs of poles

Per unit slip $= \dfrac{\text{synchronous speed} - \text{rotor speed}}{\text{synchronous speed}}$

$S = \dfrac{N_s - N_r}{N_s}$; Rotor frequency $(f_r) = Sf$

Cathode ray tubes

Force on an electron moving across a magnetic field = Bqv newtons where B is the flux density in teslas, q is the negative charge on each electron measured in coulombs and v is the velocity in m s^{-1}.

Electrostatic deflection

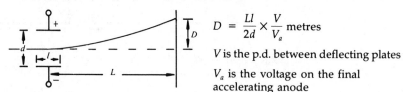

$D = \dfrac{Ll}{2d} \times \dfrac{V}{V_a}$ metres

V is the p.d. between deflecting plates

V_a is the voltage on the final accelerating anode

Electromagnetic deflection

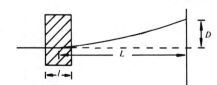

$D = BLl \sqrt{\dfrac{q}{m}} \times \dfrac{1}{2V_a}$ metres

q = negative charge on electron in coulombs = 1.6×10^{-19} C
m = mass of electron in kilogrammes = 9.11×10^{-31} kg
V_a = voltage on final accelerating anode

Transistor

Common base

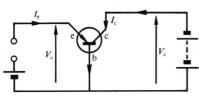

Current amplification factor $h_{fb} = \dfrac{\Delta I_c}{\Delta I_e}$

Input resistance $R_{in} = \dfrac{\Delta V_e}{\Delta I_e}\ \Omega\ =\ h_{ib}$

Output resistance $R_{out} = \dfrac{\Delta V_c}{\Delta I_c}\ \Omega\ =\ h_{ob}$

Resistance gain $= \dfrac{R_{out}}{R_{in}}$ Voltage gain $A\ =\ h_{fb} \times$ resistance gain

Power gain $P_g\ =\ h_{fb} \times A$

Common emitter

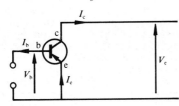

Current amplification factor $h_{fe}\ =\ \dfrac{\Delta I_c}{\Delta I_b}$

$h_{fc}\ =\ \dfrac{h_{fe}}{1 - h_{fe}}$ $R_{out}\ =\ \dfrac{\Delta V_c}{\Delta I_c}$ $R_{in}\ =\ \dfrac{\Delta V_b}{\Delta I_b}$

BOOLEAN IDENTITIES AND THEOREMS

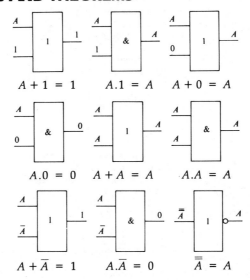

$A + 1 = 1$ $A.1 = A$ $A + 0 = A$

$A.0 = 0$ $A + A = A$ $A.A = A$

$A + \overline{A} = 1$ $A.\overline{A} = 0$ $\overline{\overline{A}} = A$

Commutative rule

$A + B\ =\ B + A$
$A.B\ =\ B.A$

Associative rule

$A + (B + C)\ =\ (A + B) + C$
$A.(B.C)\ =\ (A.B).C$

Distributive rule

$A + B.C\ =\ (A + B).(A + C)$
$A.(B + C)\ =\ A.B + A.C$
$A + A.B\ =\ A$
$A.(A + B)\ =\ A$

De Morgan's law

$\overline{A + B}\ =\ \overline{A}.\overline{B}$
$\overline{A.B}\ =\ \overline{A} + \overline{B}$

Index